Ion L. Idriess (1889—1979) is one of Australia's best-loved writers, with fifty-six books to his credit and millions of copies sold. When he returned from the First World War he wrote *The Desert Column*, about his experiences with the 5th Light Horse. *Prospecting for Gold* was his first major successful work; it immediately sold out and was reprinted constantly in the following years, as were many of his books. Idriess spent much of his life travelling throughout Australia, collecting material for his true-life stories, including *Flynn of the Inland*, *Lasseter's Last Ride* and *Back O'Cairns*. He was awarded the O.B.E. in 1968 for his contribution to Australian literature.

GW00656477

NeMarluK

Ion Idriess

Sydney Amsterdam New York

An IMPRINT book
Imprint is a division of Editions Tom Thompson
83 Victoria St, Potts Point, NSW 2011, Australia

First published in Australia in 1941 by Angus & Robertson
Reprinted in 1946, 1947, 1948, 1951, 1958
This edition published by ETT IMPRINT in 1995

Distributed by
HarperCollins *Publishers*
25 Ryde Rd, Pymble, NSW 2073, Australia
31 View Rd, Glenfield, Auckland 10, NZ
HarperCollins *International*
10 East 53rd Street, New York, NY 10022, USA
In de Knipscheer *Uitgeverij*
Singel 450, 1017 Av Amsterdam

ISBN 1 875892 10 9

Cover photograph: Nemarluk, Albany, Western Australia, 1858.
From the Macarthur Papers, State Library of New South Wales.
Cover design by Robyn Latimer
Printed in Australia by Griffin Paperbacks, Netley, SA

AUTHOR'S NOTE

THIS is the story of Nemarluk, chief of the Cahn-mah, King of the Wilds. One of the last of the Stone Age men he deserved a better fate. I know the "Wild Lands"; I knew Nemarluk personally. I hope you will know him when you have read this story of the last three years of his life. And that your sympathy will go out towards the aboriginal, the last of God's Stone Age men.

I.L.I.

CONTENTS

CHAPTER I

NEMARLUK

OUT over the swamp, far across the plain, came a piercing hunting cry. That long drawn out, haunting cry sounded even above the babble of countless waterfowl. Then there was pandemonium; for throughout this vast swamp the people in their hunting were disturbing the bird life. And now arose the whistling and warking of wild ducks, the honking of geese, the hoarse boom—boom—boom of cranes, the screeching of clouds of cockatoos, the shrieking of thousands of parrots. Far over the waterway there sounded a wind of wings as clouds of birds arose noisily to circle and then come splashing down on to the water again.

Again they rose and fell, to wail away and rise again, the hunting cry of Nemarluk, chief of the Cahn-mah, King of the Wilds.

Nemarluk was gathering his Red Band together. He stood under a clump of pandanus palms, a magnificent young savage. Wild eyes deep-set under lowering brows, eager of face as he listened for answer to his call.

Already six feet two inches tall, broad chested with a springy quickness of body, he was a picture of youth and strength, and of muscle and sinew in rippling relief. Around his arms were the plaited arm bands that the women of the tribe loved to plait for Nemarluk, while his belt was of thick rolls of plaited human hair. His chest, shoulders, and thighs deeply ridged by the weals of hard flesh that denote full warriorhood.

His shaggy hair was bound back from the forehead by a headband in which gleamed brilliant parrot feathers. Straight up from the band stood a long eagle-hawk feather. In his right hand he clasped a wommera, in his left a bundle of long spears with assagai heads, the terrible, shovel-nosed spear of the Northern Territory aboriginal. Nemarluk, hero of twenty tribes, the mightiest hunter from the Victoria River to the Daly, from the inland mountains to the sea!

Not a sound, except the distant babble of waterfowl. Down through the long pandanus leaves filtered sunlight seemed to paint the young chief's body a bronze-red. This was a polish of wild-goose oil mixed with a brick-red powder made from crushed ant-hill. Primitive old trees these, and the sun seemed to love to kiss the body of her primitive son waiting there. Nemarluk's nostrils sniffed questioningly, then he smiled in boyish pleasure.

Presently a warrior stepped beside him. Minmara, this one of the piercing eye, the rugged face, scars of spear and stone dagger plain upon his body. As he grunted a greeting his big mouth grinned from ear to ear. In minutes more Mankee the wrestler stepped beside them, then Mangul and Lin, and last of all Marragin, the crocodile hunter. He smiled. They grinned reply and rattled their spears. All were bronze-red men with the scarlet band of the killer painted upon their brow. Nemarluk's chosen men these, the Red Band.

He strode away, out towards the plain. Noiseless as panthers they followed him, their eyes already roving for first sign of animal life. For Nemarluk had tired of duck's flesh and goose eggs; he wanted meat and the excitement of a hard chase.

It was a glorious morning with a blue sky far above this Did-ee plain that stretched nearly north and south farther than the eye could see. A sea of luxuriant grass with green islands upon it that were the palms and tall paper-barks of the swamps.

Distantly under a shimmer of sunlight, heavy grey shapes were pushing through the grass. A mob of buffalo these, fat and suspicious at what had made the birds take to flight. Through the plain meanders the Moyle River, its waters now almost lost to view in the long grass. A black, muddy bottom has the Moyle, home of countless wildfowl.

As the Red Band stepped out on to the plain a drum beat lightly.—No, it was only a male swamp pheasant. He rose from the grass at their feet and alighted on a shrub his long tail swaying, his coal black coat agleam. The bush, the dearly beloved bush of primitive man, was singing with new life.

To Nemarluk's eyes that bush stretched on and on and on, without end. He felt so happy he raised his voice in the triumph cry and a piercing "Yak-ai! Yak-ai! Yak-ai!" sped out far over the plain. Presently, very faintly from far away, there came floating an answering "Yak-ai!" They grinned, recognizing the call of Tiger, he of Tiger's Mob. And so—Tiger also wanted meat.

Light of heart the Red Band walked on. Nature's children these, primitive sons of primitive men. This the land they loved, the life they loved. They felt very brave—and they *were* brave. These and their tribesmen in Australia's last few isolated places are the last of the Stone Age men. Alas—their most terrible weapon was and is only the shovel-nosed spear.

"At seventy long steps I can kill a buffalo with this," grunted Marragin, "kill a white man's bullock, too. And what a mess it makes of a man!" Lovingly he balanced the weapon.

"Don't blunt its edge," laughed Nemarluk. "Soon you may want to use it."

"There now!" hissed Mangul, and they glanced towards two big buffalo horns moving above the grass.

They ducked down and crouching, swiftly separated to get around the beast. The hunt had begun. At sundown they would return to camp loaded with meat. For the Red Band never failed.

Now let us follow intelligently this story, for it is a true page from our frontier history; every man and woman mentioned lived or is living now. It is a story of white and brown and black, a story of endurance that fought on and on until the very last. It is the story of the hopeless fight of Stone Age man.

This was the wildest area in the Northern Territory, some hundreds of miles south-west of Darwin. This country, like a few similar areas in Australia, is known as the Wild Lands. Towards the east it is bounded by the Daly River, to the south by the Victoria. Its north and north-west is the wild coast. Far inland it is hemmed in by a maze of ranges that are a labyrinth of canyons and gorges and walls of cliffs protecting inaccessible native hideouts. Several hundreds of miles in length and depth, this country is nearly the last fastness of the Stone Age man. Fronting the ranges are the foothills. And then the plain country; the Moyle River country with its miles upon miles of swamps; the Did-ee and other big plains.

Running from the mountains through the plain country nearly midway to the south, to empty eventually near the mouth of the Victoria River runs the Fitzmaurice River, probably the gloomiest, loneliest, most dangerous river in Australia. For here was the haunt of King Chugulla and Tiger's Mob. The plains end near the coast in forest or sand dune country, then mangrove. The coastal boundary of the Wild Lands is thus the sea. The southern side is bounded by the Victoria River, the eastern by the Daly. Inland by the long walls of ranges.

Along the lonely coast there are no white men. Well up from its broad mouth the Daly River supports a tiny white settlement, while away to the south on the Victoria are some of the greatest cattle stations in the world. Just half a dozen great stations, the homesteads almost all on the opposite bank of the river from the Wild Lands, towards the West Australian boundary.

Some of the aboriginal tribes enclosed by the two rivers, the coast and the mountains, are the Brinken, the Dilek, the Cahn-mah, Tgerait, Dini-Dim, Pongo-Pongo, Mulluk-Mulluk, sub-tribes of the Wogait, a branch of the Wolwanga, with others and unknown tribes in among the ranges.

Some members of most of the tribes at times visited the little white settlement on the Daly, and the cattle stations on the distant Victoria. Cautiously they would approach the native camp at either settlement or station and, if the coast was clear, would come in and mix with the station boys, trading for tobacco and iron. For the wild aboriginal craves tobacco with a great craving. The iron they prized highly for spearheads. Iron spearheads and iron knives were far more deadly, far more useful than stone or bone. The station blacks greeted the wild visitors eagerly for they brought news of distant friends, of corroborees, of vendettas, of tribal wars, and the movements of game in the wild bush. In return, the station and settlement boys whispered news of the movements of the "white pleece". When they had got all they wanted and learned all they could the visitors would vanish.

Sometimes though they would arrive to the accompaniment of shrieks, howling of dogs, yells of angry tribesmen. For these wild men from the bush would steal a young lubra at times and spear any who attempted to stop them. Sometimes they came on vengeance bound. A shower of spears, a man writhing on the ground and the wild men were away.

To guard the white settlers on the Daly and the lonely station people on the Victoria the authorities had established two small police stations; one on the Daly, the other at Timber Creek, just up above the crossing by the Victoria River. That tiny little police outpost is one of the most isolated in the whole vast Territory. But because of its position on the edge of the Wild Lands it is one of the most important.

The mounted patrols always had plenty of work to do in the very sparsely settled country away from the Wild Lands. They only interfered with the natives there when bands of the wild men sneaked on station or settlement and speared natives working for the settlers. Thus happened again and again throughout year after year, these ceaseless native blood feuds.

Occasionally, a settler was killed. More often it would be a nomad, perhaps a prospector or dingo hunter who despite police warnings would push on out into the Wild Lands. When months went by and such a wanderer did not return then the police would order their smartest trackers to quietly make inquiries. And presently, through the friends of this "black intelligence" would come a whisper of the killing of the lonely man. Then would come the job of running in the horses, shoeing them, loading up the packs, and the long, long chase would begin.

Quite apart from the Wild Lands the whole vast Territory was and is policed similarly by widely scattered police outposts. The hilly country and the coast, the plains and buffalo-land, Arnhem Land and the Wild Lands, south of Darwin at the Catherine, to far away back into the spinifex country, the desert, and the Centre. And the men who manned and man these lonely outposts are among the finest types in Australia. Cheery under all circumstances but with a grim tenacity that never gives in, men of almost tireless endurance born to an outdoor life, men who love the wild and know the ways of the wild, men with initiative to overcome any obstacles and just go on, on, on.

Time and again their patrols have been beaten, their horses knocked up or perished, their stores all gone, their trackers wounded or babbling with fever. At such times the patrol would battle its way far back to the little outpost, run in fresh horses, secure fresh trackers, then start out again and keep on and on.

This was the type of man the warrior of the Wild Lands were up against should they break the white man's law. And well the wild men knew it. Had it not been so, there would have been many, many more tragedies happen to the lonely whites in the far out places.

And now just a word about the trackers and then you'll understand better the type of human bloodhounds who soon were to be upon the trail of Nemarluk. You will understand how a clever, ferocious killer like Tiger who knew every stone upon his native land, a powerful, resolute man possessed of almost superhuman endurance and a boundless cunning, could be tracked, and tracked, and tracked until at last he was run to earth.

The best trackers come from the "bad men". These are the clever native outlaws who, notorious cattle spearers, have again and again eluded the traps set

B

for them and returned to spear again. These are the restless, aggressive men among their own tribe who are always up to mischief and have the shrewdness and initiative to "get away with it". Especially if such a man be outlawed from his own tribe because of native vendetta or because he had broken some native law would the police consider his services as a tracker, should he offer. Because such a man knew all the laws of the wild, and all the tricks of the game. He had hunted men, and been hunted by men. And the fact that he was still alive and free proved he was a better man than all who had hunted him. He knew every trick of covering up tracks; knew every sign of the bush, every trick of ambush and surprise, of hideout and flight, of runaway and of flight. Set this man on the tracks of an outlaw and the outlaw, in the long run, would have little chance. He might be as good, even better than the tracker; still, behind the tracker would be the white police forcing the tracker, on, on, on; never allowing him to give in.

Yet another great advantage a clever tracker has; he can "smell out" information. For the aboriginal will often put another away providing the wanted man be not his own kinsman. Many tribes are really foreigners to one another. Further, the tracker knows many of the undercurrents of intrigue and jealousy that are present in the life of every tribe. He has, too, his totem brothers and totem kinsmen. And these are a secret society who, when called upon, must help one another.

Again and again, however, some exceptionally clever native outlaw has beaten a persistent and clever tracker. What has then caught the outlaw has been the thinking power behind the tracker—the deduction of the policeman. His brain is constantly working far ahead of and many miles around his own tracker. From the result of the tracker's work the policeman is spinning a mental spiderweb as it were around the fleeing, or hiding man.

From where the tracker fails the policeman quickly decides. The last tracks tell whether the hunted one is exhausted or still full of strength, whether he knows that the pursuers are close upon his tracks or is unaware that danger is near. Those last faint tracks tell very many things. From them the policeman will know whether the hunted one is urgently seeking water or friends or food, or whether he is merely on walkabout or hunting.

The policeman must first find the nearest water, and know or find where lies the best game country, and know or find where the man's friends may be. He must deduct what the wanted man will do next and—anticipate his moves.

Thus, the ceaseless battle of endurance and wits goes on between black and white.

CHAPTER II

WAR ON THE WHITE MEN

UNDER a full moon the firelit pandanus palms looked beautiful. Squads of dancing men weirdly painted, their eyes glaring from circles of ochre, surmounted by head-dresses of feathers and dyed grasses, clashed their fighting weapons to the maddening rhythm of the dance. A quick drumbeat was ringing out over the plain as two hundred chanting women slapped their laps. The clicking of kylie sticks and the bellow of the didjeridoo accompanied savage bursts of song. Warriors leaped high to rattle their spears then stamp the ground to furious grunts. All were becoming worked up for the final act of the Meeting of the Tribes. At this period of the year numerous tribes met to feast, then staged the initiation ceremonies that brought the young men into warriorhood.

Soon would come the dry season when many of the lagoons would dry up, and the game seek grass wherever it still grew green. Within a week all the tribes would scatter, each to their own hunting grounds. Then, if any man trespassed on another's, without tribal reason, he would be speared.

Now they were working up to the fights. To-morrow would be settled many an old score. There would certainly be a tribal fight also; perhaps even a battle in which each tribe would turn raging upon the other until all were engaged.

Faster went the dance. Now a quick, maddening throb was in the drumbeats, a quivering stamp in the feet of the warriors that resembled angry thunder; the women's voices shrieked a chant of revenge.

In the great circle squatting around the dancers no eyes gleamed so malevolently as Wadjee's, the shrivelled-up old witch doctor, squatting alone in the shadows just apart from the Council of the Old Men. Beady eyes were set deep either side of a broken nose. Cruel thoughts burned behind wrinkled brow. His skinny arms hung loosely across his knees; his necklace of bones was dull with age. Beside him lay the charm bag in which, sheathed in paper-bark, was the dreaded Bone. Other charms were there, too: shrivelled up eagle talons and crocodile eyes and "spirit" bones of men, queer-shaped charms of agate and ribbon stone, sticks mysteriously carved.

But the charms that smoke-grimed bag held were mostly evil. Old Wadjee was the most dreaded witch doctor of all the tribes. Each tribe had its witch doctor, the cunning man who lived by preying upon the fears of the warriors, but who stirred up trouble only for his own gain.

In pleasing contrast to these shrewd old schemers was Nemarluk in all his bravery, laughing in corroboree as he led the Cahn-mah. The bright eyes of Marboo never left him; she was singing only for him, her warrior chief. For Marboo was now Nemarluk's young wife, the happiest, proudest little woman in all the Wild Lands. She never noticed the sneer on the mouth of old Wadjee as he glared at her, then at Nemarluk. Nemarluk, the favourite, who already had great influence amongst all these people.

Facing the Brinken men while leading his own warriors was Tiger. A solidly built young savage with lowering brow, his eyes were furious as he fumed and raged. In moments now he would lead his men against

the Brinken who dared him challenge for challenge.
Old warriors were already leaping into the air, chewing their beards, rattling their spears in the final fit
of rage.

Tiger was really the brother of Nemarluk, not such
a giant but strong and fierce. Whereas Nemarluk was
very boyish and ready to rush into any adventure, Tiger
always thought first. Though Nemarluk could fly into
a terrible rage, Tiger would always think coldly, cunningly, ferociously.

These two fierce cubs of a warrior chief liked one
another but could never have lived with the one tribe.
Neither could be second dog. So, Tiger had thought
it out. Then picked up his weapons and scowling, vanished towards the ranges. He fought his way to the
leadership of a horde. And his fighting men were
raging around him now: Chugulla the king with his
shaggy head towering above the big warriors there;
cunning old Walung, an Inkata of the Council, rattling
his spears beside the heavily built, frowning Wanda-
warry who had the grizzled old Alligator at his spear
arm. Tall and round backed and very skinny was old
Alligator of the shrewd eyes; he was urging on the
laughing giant Chalmer whose battle roar was like the
bellow of a bull. The cunning Maru stamped beside
them; and Chin-amon the spear thrower; and the
sinewy Coonbook, with Anglartchie and others of his
chosen band.

All fighting men these; ruthless, cunning, and strong.
They held sway over all Chugulla's country along the
Fitzmaurice to the Victoria, as Nemarluk's Red Band
ruled Nemarluk's country away back to the Daly. The
cattlemen on the distant Victoria River called this band
"Tiger's Mob" knowing the fierce cunning of Tulan

the Tiger. Though Tiger used constantly to visit and study the whites, Nemarluk always kept to the bush.

A spear hurtled through the air to be followed by another then another. To a sudden terrible drumming, warriors sprang forward with spears quivering in their wommeras as Nemarluk leaped in the air with a shout that turned all eyes upon him. He waved down their spears and shouted:

"I declare war!"

A shout rose to the skies echoed by the shriek of the women.

"On the white men—and the Jap men!" roared Nemarluk.

Utter silence. Staring eyes, spears poised, rage frozen to amazed faces. Overhead came the heavy swish of wings, the honk, honk, honk! of a flock of wild geese.

"War on the white men!" roared Nemarluk. "War on the Jap men!"

Tiger's sullen face was staring towards Nemarluk, his cunning eyes gleaming. The words of Nemarluk voiced the wish of his life. He glanced at the painted faces all staring there in the moonlight, then leaped beside Nemarluk and furiously rattled his spears.

"War on the white men!" he roared. "War on the Jap men!"

Women leaped up screaming. Warriors rattled their spears and broke into the deep-chested war chant. Presently, Nemarluk shouted them to silence: "We are fools to fight one another," he shouted. "The white men are all around our country. Even though far away, nearer and nearer they come. They come to take our lands, our hunting grounds. When they enter our own country, let us kill them."

To the roar of approval Nemarluk's Red Band and Tiger's Mob were suddenly joined by warriors, the heroes of all the tribes. These were warriors who had killed white men, men whom the white police sought, men who had escaped a hundred traps. There were men here who had ambushed a police patrol, who had lain in wait for the cattlemen, who had dared the white men's guns. Sweating under their war paint they rattled their spears like madmen under this influence of war hysteria. Pundek was raving with excitement as he pushed his way to the front. Pundek had distinguished himself with the band who attacked the lugger *Pat* in the dead of night; it was Pundek's tomahawk which swiped at Constable Kenneth's head but chopped his fingers instead. Widjullee leaped beside Pundek, Widjullee who had speared the white man Watts and fed his body to the crocodiles. Widjullee was painted in the crocodile totem now. He rattled his spears not knowing that soon the inexorable law of the wild would be on his tracks—an eye for an eye, a tooth for a tooth.

Cunningly Tiger welcomed these noted men as the warriors surged around them: cocksure Mooderish with big mouth and aggressive face, heavy, hairy body; Nujooloo, killer of the white man Renouf, leered beside him. And by them now crowded Nudjie and Nanynyah and Cambit; their band had attacked Constables Hemming and Hoffman's patrol and speared trackers, Charlie and Bogey. That wild foray was praised in song and dance at many a corroboree fire. Other excited warriors who had speared men, white, brown, yellow and black, with noted cattle spearers, leaped in among them. Soon all the killers had joined Nemarluk and Tiger. Fiercely they swore to kill any white men who entered their country, any Jap men who landed on their coasts.

"The Jap men come often in their ships," shouted

Nemarluk. "By and by they will come like hawks gathering to the kill. Then they will take our country from us."

"Kill! Kill! Kill!" roared hundreds of throats. Tribal enmity was forgotten. This war against white and Jap men took their breath away. The Inkatas of the Council were silently squatting just within the ring of fires, not adding their voices as yet to the shouts of the warriors. But their old eyes were gleaming, and their deep-lined faces seemed to take on new life.

And just within the shadows another pair of old eyes were gleaming, evil as a snake's: "War on the white men and the Jap men!" How had such a thought come into the mind of a fool boy? Maliciously he watched Nemarluk, he whose name would ring far out across the Wild Lands.

Sobering at last, the crowd of warriors broke into talking groups, then as with one accord grew silent and came and squatted around the Council of the Old Men. Patiently they awaited the wisdom of these men. The night grew very silent. At last the chief Inkata grunted, began to talk. They talked until the moon waned and the eastern sky lightened rosy pink to a rising sun. From the swamp arose the cackle of awakening wildfowl. And still they talked.

"The white police?" queried a timid one.

Mooderish roared with laughter.

"Wah! We will kill them too!" And the women broke into shrieks of laughter, throwing mud at the timid one.

"Bul-bul?" frowned a wizened little hunter.

Nemarluk sprang to his feet quivering with rage.

"I will kill him! I will kill Bul-bul!" He stood trembling there with his big hands clenching and unclenching, glaring upon them all. Silently they stared. Uneasy, too, several of them looked.

For Bul-bul was the most dreaded tracker in all the vast territory. As cunning as the best amongst them, as fearless as the best, and a bigger man even than Nemarluk. Bul-bul was nearly as big as the two giants Chugulla and Chalmer. And Bul-bul loved hunting, loved hunting men.

A week later the tribes separated, scattering north, south, east, and west to a hullabaloo of shouting and spear waving; loud tribal calls from the men, shrill voices of the women ringing far over plain and swamp: "Ma-muck!" "Ma-muck!" "Ma—muck!" Imitative shrieks from the children, the young boys very brave as they hurled reed spears in mock battle. The long drawn calls grew fainter and fainter till there was only the sunlight and the great blue sky and the silence of the Australian bush. At the faint tracks upon the ground a dingo sniffed warily.

After the corroboree time serious life must begin again for the little tribes and hordes of primitive men, women and children now steadily marching towards their own beloved hunting grounds. Again, as each year, there dawned the struggle for existence. Soon, the long dry season would be upon them. Each must live by his hunting skill and by the cleverness of the women in finding vegetable food, or else starve.

The Cahn-mah marched happily towards their beloved coast; towards the scrubby little hillocks rich in vegetable food, the innumerable mangrove creeks and arms of the sea and short, gloomy, salt-water mouths, the beaches and mud flats and reefs that held fish and shell-fish, turtle and occasional dugong.

And among all these now scattered tribes there was a burning desire in the heart of many a warrior to drive his spear into the chest of white man or brown.

CHAPTER III

THE COMING OF THE BROWN MEN'S SHIP

NEMARLUK, the laughing chief, with his Red Band strode out in the lead, all eager-faced, walking with the long, springy, tireless tread of the aboriginal. Nemarluk had spread out his men to right and left of him about two hundred yards apart. And away out on each side of them were the warrior lads, Coon-an-pore, Me-al-cull, Nungpare, Tunma; then the men warriors, Montspere, Nargoo, Kum-munga, Wahroo, Mah-lan, and all the men of the Cahn-mah. With them travelled skinny old Alligator with the shrewd eyes, and the stocky, sullen Maru. Both these warriors were men of Tiger's Mob going aholidaying with the Cahn-mah.

They were now in a country of earth mounds capped by stunted bushes. As the long line strode on there was a glimpse of a feathered head here and there, sun glint on chocolate body, spearheads moving forward among the bushes. Every eye read at a glance the faintest track of animal, bird, or reptile; whether upon the ground, the grass, or up in the trees.

A wallaby broke cover just dodging Nargoo's spear to run almost into Wahroo. A howl of derision arose as he missed the close shot. The wallaby doubled back with men racing across to cut it off. Confused by a spear that hissed past its eyes it doubled back again. Now huntsmen almost surrounded it. Swerving again to another spear and a yell, it ran into the spear of Mah-lan. A yell of congratulation greeted this throw. After the grinning Mah-lan had killed his prize and slung it around his neck, the huntsmen spread out again and marched on. They would thus march and hunt until all met, at sunset, wherever their night's camp might lie.

In line also but slightly behind the warriors came the lads who next season would be initiated into their first degree of warriorhood. Eager-faced lads these, fully armed and keen to use their weapons. This was their school time, their school of life. They watched every movement of the men ahead, studying the reason why; for the time would soon come when they too must join the warrior ranks to spend their lives in fighting for, in feeding, and protecting the tribe.

Well behind the lads the women came dawdling; spread out, too, but in little groups that continually stopped to squat and dig with their sharp-pointed digging sticks for yams, edible bulbs and roots; or hunting snakes and lizards, and seeking the cosy camp of bandicoot, porcupine, rat—and the lovely little Nundjala.

With a shrill of delight Marboo found one cuddled up in a cosy nest deep under a tuft of grass. The women grouped around her as she pulled the struggling little creature out. Its body was about one foot long with a longer black tail having a snow-white tip. Its little finger tips and toe tips were white like the tip of its tail and belly, but all the rest of its coat was a greenish grey fur. Frightened big black eyes looked from a quaintly large head. Its arched snout struggled violently in Marboo's hand, its long whiskers twitching, its big ears standing straight up. Fiercely it struggled, getting into an awful temper, and suddenly sank its two long incisor teeth into Marboo's wrist. She dropped it like a red-hot coal and it was away at a swift bounding run, marvellously dodging the dogs and women who were after it with a yell. Experts though they were they couldn't catch it. Presently, it leaped for a tree and sped straight up at a great rate to disappear into a hollow.

That Nundjala would never camp on the ground again; he should never have left his cosy hollow deep in the tree trunk. A lovely creature of the night is the Nundjala.

When the women came straggling into camp at sundown their dilly-bags would be full of roots and bulbs and berries and vegetable fruits. Some would be loaded with snake and flying possum, water-rat and pelke and porcupine; so that should the men find no larger game the tribe would not go hungry to sleep.

With the women were the young girls learning to know the vines and shrubs, the grasses and creepers whose roots and bulbs were good to eat; the value of screw palm and pandanus palm, of zamia palm and bamboo and the many trees whose fruit or shoot, pith or leaf or nut are good to eat. Learning, too, the track of snake and bandicoot, of "dry-land" turtle and water tortoise, of ground bird and water-rat, of porcupine and goanna, of Nundjala and pelke, and of the many other creatures and things that live and grow upon the earth. They learned, too, to recognize and distinguish signs on the trees—the scratch that meant possum or phalanger, Nundjala or pelke, goanna claw or beak of bird; to follow the flight of the wild bee; and to remember the surprising varieties of foods to be found in and around swamps and lagoons.

Nature is a brutal master. He who does not know where to find his food must starve.

The Cahn-mah had happy days on their march back to the coast. For it would be some months yet before the dry season dried up the waters and grasses and

made scarce the game. Everywhere there was plenty to
eat if a man only knew where to look for it. The
Grevilleas were coming out in yellow flower on which
dined honeysucker and shrieking parrot. Many shallow
lagoons still swarmed with wildfowl. The still soft
earth told a story to those who would read its letterings.

And so the happy days passed. Old Alligator and
cunning Maru, Tiger's two men, were very keen on
"war talk", little dreaming how soon they would see it.

One morning a month later, back at the old home
camp, the Cahn-mah were squatting around the cooking fires dining on roasted fish when a warning call
sounded. They stared towards Coor-i-ming look out.
Yes, a smoke signal was rising softly into the quiet
morning air.

"Sail!"

Marboo looked at Nemarluk, her little heart beating
fast. Only she had a premonition of what this might
mean. The warriors stared meaningly at each other
then snatched weapons and rushed towards a vantage
point.

Yes, it was a ship, the sun glinting on its sails. The
warriors stared at Nemarluk. But the die had been cast.

"If they come into our water," he said fiercely, "we
will kill them!"

They squatted down then, staring at the tiny sail so
far away.

"She is heading this way," said Lin of the eagle eye.

"She will come," growled Minmara, "like they all
come—to take our land. This time, we shall kill them."

His heavy, sullen face was suddenly distorted by
rage. He shook his fist towards the far distant sail.

"Let us talk," suggested an old Inkata, cunningly,
"lest they do the killing, not us."

"Call the Old Men together," growled Nemarluk.

"Plan now, for soon it will be too late. We must take them unawares, otherwise their fire-guns will kill us."

"I have a plan," said the old Inkata.

It was a good plan, a cunning plan. A plan which, if it worked would separate the crew aboard and, above all, would give them hardly a chance to use their fire-arms.

All the afternoon they sat there gazing out to sea, their fierce eyes gleaming under shaggy brows. Their talk dwindled to an occasional grunt. The sail had drawn much closer. She was a pearling lugger and, definitely, was heading for their waters.

"If only they will land!" shouted Nemarluk. "We will kill them and take all the iron and tobacco they have."

A roar of approval greeted this lust for tobacco. At the start of this great war of their's they had actually forgotten loot and tobacco.

Tobacco and iron! The only two things which the aboriginal craves of our civilization. He wants nothing more of us. The thing he most dearly loves is—freedom. And we take that from him.

Late that afternoon the *Ouida* sailed into Port Keats. Not a real port this, it is only a name, a bay in a wild coast with mangrove and plain and hills all around. Cautiously the lugger crept on, right into Treachery Bay.

Sharp eyes were aboard that little lugger; very uneasy eyes. Well they knew the danger. But the winds had been calm, and they had almost run right out of water. They must load up with water somewhere, and with wood too. This vessel was on a shark fishing cruise, for at this time the price of pearl-shell was very low.

Seeking an anchorage from which if danger threatened they could slip away easily, the little craft slowly crept up the bay. The crew aboard stared into the dense fringe of trees to either side. Even the keen eyes of the suspicious Melville Island boys could detect no sign of life.

But hidden eyes were watching them, eyes that saw all things.

"Jap men!" growled Minmara.

Mankee held up three fingers. "We will easily kill them," he grinned. "What a pity there are not a lot more!"

"The others are Melville Island tribesmen," sneered Mangul, and handled his bone dagger. "I would like the kidney fat of a Melville Island boy."

"Your chance will soon come," growled Kerinbo.

"He! he!" laughed skinny old Alligator. "They don't know we won't give them a chance to use their guns."

Nemarluk's laughing face grew serious now that action was nearly come. After all, it was really he who had suggested this war.

On board the lugger *Ouida* were the Japanese Nagata, Yoshida, and Owashi with a crew of Melville Island aboriginals. These boys were foreigners to the tribe ashore and well knew what would happen to them should they be taken by surprise. But there was no sign of life anywhere. They dropped anchor; downed sails, furled them; made all shipshape. Only then did a canoe shoot from the mangroves. The Melville Island crew boys were instantly on the alert, their spears and tomahawks beside them. The Japanese glanced at their guns, ready to hand.

But there were only three men in the canoe. As it paddled swiftly alongside the crew boys saw there were no spears in the bottom of the canoe, could see no bone dangers concealed in the tangled hair and beards of the men. And then a big, laughing savage leaped aboard, and strode straight up to the Japanese, taking no notice of the crew. He laughed at the Japanese, saying something in rollicking voice. The little brown men stared up at this muscular savage surprised to see now that he was but little more than a boy. His fearlessness, too, surprised them. This was no cringing, cadging aboriginal, his swift glance around the deck was more like that of a captain, an owner.

Minmara and Lin then leaped aboard and immediately squatted on deck. Though their shaggy eyes appeared not interested really they took in everything at a glance: the rifles, the tomahawks around the mast and handy by the cabin top, the spears evenly placed around the vessel, the sullen looks of the Melville Islanders now ranging them in.

Nemarluk's men saw that in case of sudden alarm a man, no matter where he might be at the moment could grasp a weapon anywhere.

The Melville Island boys deeply suspicious, watched closely, and watched the shore too, expecting a fleet of canoes any moment.

The Japanese asked Nemarluk if there was fresh water handy ashore. The Melville Islanders after some difficulty managed to translate question and reply.

"There's plenty of fresh water ashore," assured Nemarluk, "plenty of wood, too. My people will lend you a hand to load the boat. But," he laughed and smacked his stomach, "there's better than water and wood. There're plenty of wild geese in the lagoon. Load up the ship with ducks and geese if only you have those shooting irons that kill things!"

And Nemarluk laughed his invitation to the skies. His eyes were dancing with pleasure, he waved his big arms towards the shore in imitation of flights of geese.

c

He showed his fine white teeth and went through the motions of tearing a wild duck to pieces.

The Japanese spoke amongst themselves.

"It may be safe," said the captain, dubiously. "These men wear no war paint; they carry no weapons. They are gluttons. They are thinking of the geese we can kill as against their own crude weapons. It is a grand opportunity to load water and at the same time fill up the larder with ducks and geese. We can shoot plenty for the savages, too, and that will keep them in a good humour. They will help us then with the water and wood. We will be perfectly safe as long as we are wary. We have fire-arms; they have only spears and clubs."

And his two companions, needing water badly, and eager at the prospect of fresh meat, agreed.

CHAPTER IV

THE KILLING OF THE BROWN MEN

NEMARLUK, grinning happily, put his hand to his tangled hair and pulled out a crab's claw pipe. He flourished the claw with a smile. (It is from the big claw of the crab that the coastal aboriginals fashion a pipe.) Captain Nagata smiled and handed to Nemarluk and Minmara and Lin half a stick of trade tobacco each. They grabbed it with eager hands, stuffed their pipes, then going to the galley picked up a live coal and dropped it on the pipe. Puffing contentedly they squatted upon the deck, evidently contented to stay, to eat all they could, and make good fellows of themselves.

They slept aboard that night; slept soundly coiled up on the deck. The Melville Island boys hardly slept at all. Blear-eyed, they frowned towards the dark shapes of their sleeping visitors; then, gripping spears, stared through dusky night towards the shore. But no shadowy canoes put off, no dark heads suddenly bobbed up beside the lugger. Dawn came and the visitors were still snoring contentedly.

Later, they ate a lazy breakfast of rice; yawned; seemed in no hurry to go ashore. A grey crane flew across the bay with raucous cry. The snout of a crocodile rose up a hundred yards away; the cold eyes of the saurian regarded the lugger a moment then slowly sank. The visitors cadged another smoke, amiably squatting on deck. The Japanese watched them closely but these appeared to be men with no guile. Several hours passed. Then Nemarluk, with a broad smile suggested he should row ashore and bring some young women aboard to pluck the ducks and geese. He would even bring his own young wife, Marboo. All the women were good workers, quick at cleaning ducks and geese and fish.

The Japanese hesitated and were lost.

"If this man," said Captain Nagata, seriously, "is game to bring his own wife aboard to help in cleaning the geese then surely they can mean us no harm. They dare not. For if they attacked us then we would have their own women aboard as hostages." His mates, after a little talk, agreed.

Nemarluk proved as good as his word. He canoed ashore and returned with five young women, among them Marboo. The Japanese now felt nearly sure that the aboriginals could mean them no harm. They set about further proving the goodwill of the strangers by ordering them to load the lugger with water. Soon, other aboriginals appeared as busily the canoes began plying between shore and lugger, bringing aboard kerosene tins full of water, and loads of firewood. A busy day, that. The sun went down, and all was well. For two days the work of loading went on, all in good comradeship. The edge of the Japanese suspicion was gradually blunted. On the third morning Nemarluk and his Red Band came lazily canoeing to the *Ouida,* the canoe song of the Cahn-mah echoing sweetly across the still water. The Red Band were unarmed. Leaping aboard in most friendly fashion, they squatted on the deck laughing and gossiping as canoe after canoe came to the lugger to be unloaded then paddled back to the shore for another load.

Nagata the captain made up his mind to go ashore and shoot ducks—many ducks. He stepped into the dinghy and ordered a Melville crew boy to the oars.

Sullenly the boy obeyed. Side by side canoe and dinghy paddled to the shore. The Melville Islander stood suspiciously by the dinghy while the captain stepped ashore. The unarmed aboriginals and the captain stepped into the bush.

They took him to the lagoon, he could hear the call of ducks. Nemarluk signalled caution and on tiptoe stepped ahead to part the vines. He beckoned with a grin. Nagata stepped forward and his eyes gleamed at the sight of many ducks swimming upon the water. He raised his gun.

"Bang!"

A cloud of cackling wildfowl rose up to the echo of the gunshot.

"Bang!"

Ducks fell from a flock wheeling overhead. The Red Band laughed their delight as they waded out to secure the fallen ducks. The shooting was excellent. Cloud after cloud of ducks and geese rose whistling and trumpeting to gunshot after gunshot. Nagata was lured farther and farther in among the waterlogged timbers of the lagoon. And, then, when he was far from human aid they suddenly turned and killed him.

"Quick!" hissed Nemarluk. They snatched up the geese and hurried back towards the dinghy to appear lazily sauntering among the trees. The Melville Islander was still standing by the dinghy.

"Nagata told us to bring the geese aboard," explained Nemarluk as he threw his load into the canoe. "He is going to shoot us a kangaroo for ourselves. He will come along himself by and by." And the Red Band stepped into the canoe.

The Melville Islander stared in a frightened way.

"You wait for Nagata," ordered Nemarluk. "He will come soon."

Lin picked up the paddle and the canoe shot out toward the *Ouida*. Marragin stood in the bows triumphantly displaying the geese. But the Melville Islanders aboard stared down into the canoe.

"Where Nagata?" demanded the Japanese as the Red Band leaped aboard.

"He shoot kangaroo," explained Nemarluk, and told how Nagata had ordered them aboard with the geese. The Japanese frowned but the Red Band strolled unconcernedly forward and squatting down by the women, began to smoke. The Melville Islanders suddenly slipped overboard into the canoe.

"Where you go?" demanded Yoshida.

"Go ashore look longa Nagata," they replied.

"Come back quick," frowned Yoshida.

"Arright." And they paddled away.

All seemed quite normal aboard, there was nothing to worry about. The aboriginals were chatting and laughing forrard, a blue crane flapped lazily overhead. With one more glance around the Japanese squatted down by the geese, adored their plumpness, and began to pluck them. Nemarluk's eyes widened meaningly.

The Red Band leaped up, seized tomahawks and in an instant were upon the Japanese. It was all over in seconds. With heaving chests they stood panting there with the blood-lust in their eyes. A shriek of triumph rang out from the shore now lined with painted figures rushing canoes to the water. The Melville Islanders shot outstream, their paddles plying in a race for life. Nemarluk's Red Band were howling their triumph song on the blood-stained deck. The first action of their war, almost a complete triumph.

Almost! The Melville Islanders were racing towards the sea. The canoes did not follow them, they shot straight out towards the lugger wild at the prospects of loot.

"We'll get them just when we want them," laughed Nemarluk as he looked towards the fleeing Melville Islanders.

But the crew boys were racing for their lives. With the yells of the Cahn-mah behind them, they bent to the oars and fairly lifted the dinghy from the water.

"Up anchor!" roared Nemarluk, "they'll get away."

Men and women were swarming aboard as canoe after canoe dashed up.

"Up anchor!" roared Nemarluk. "Haul! Pull!"

But the struggling mob, wildly excited, were unused to ships. A mob of men and women rushed to the anchor chain all in one another's way, pulling in all directions, all howling and laughing. Old Alligator slipped and in going overboard pulled two others with him. A shriek of laughter arose, echoed by the three heads rising to the surface. All hands dropped the chain and the anchor rattled to the bottom again.

"I'll kill you all!" roared Nemarluk, and knocked men right and left. "Pull up that anchor. Pull up those sails."

Sobered by his wrath they manned the chain, clumsily unfurled the sails, hauled them up in a very unseamanlike way. But the sails filled, the *Ouida* began to forge ahead. The chase had started.

The crew boys were now far down the bay and pulling swiftly with the effortless stroke of accomplished seamen. In less than half an hour Nemarluk's men had learned how to handle tiller and sails. They were expert canoemen and soon had the feel of the *Ouida*; an hour later under a stiff breeze she began to make up leeway fast. Nemarluk roared with laughter;

they all laughed, warriors and women and a crowd of youngsters. Eagerly they stared out towards the racing dinghy. An hour later and they were noticeably gaining, the slap of waves now dashed them with spray and caused roar after roar of laughter. Ah! they were gaining swiftly now, speeding along the coast; the straining men in that dinghy ahead were tiring fast.

The Red Band leaped to the bows, roared their war song and rattled their spears, leaping high upon the deck. And all hands shrieked with laughter as the men ahead bent yet again to the oars and sprinted a little ahead.

"Crash!" The *Ouida* rolled drunkenly, spilling half the people overboard, then all were over as boom and sail swung hard over. The ship lay on her beam ends hard and fast upon a sandbank.

The hunted men had lured them into a trap, had raced the dinghy over a shallow bank upon which the *Ouida* had crashed.

Scores of dark bodies treading water, gaspingly stared at the wreck. Nemarluk shouted his rage, rising in the water to shake his fist at the fleeing dinghy. Then he laughed.

"Never mind," he shouted. "They'll get away now. Never mind, we'll loot the ship."

They plunged back to the *Ouida* and scrambling aboard fought to get down below. Wild shouts as the stronger ones down there pulled out cases and bags and jars and bottles of foodstuffs, howls of delight when they smashed a case of tobacco. Everything was brought up on the sloping deck. Cases were smashed; bags were ripped open while they swarmed like ants around sweet meat. From an oily rag old Alligator pulled a shiny little iron thing. Loud "Wahs!" as they stared at the proud finder. Grinning widely he smelt the little barrel, squinted down it, began playing with the mechanism.

"Bang!" and the bullet whistled within an inch of Marragin's ear. Shocked silence. Then Marragin fell upon Alligator and they wrestled to fall and roll across the sloping deck overboard. The laughter cooled them off again. But all hands were very wary now of anything that looked like a fire-arm.

Then Marboo gave a little shriek of delight. She was staring into a looking-glass. The young women crowded around her; all tried to peer into the glass; Cawnpore snatched it from Marboo; Marboo snatched it back again. Alligator snatched it from her. He saw a hideous old face lined with a thousand wrinkles around a big flat nose, and all around it was tangled hair and beard amongst which was a huge mouth. Alligator gazed unbelievingly then opened his mouth to roar with hysterical laughter. Nemarluk snatched the glass and peered in to see what Alligator had seen. He saw himself and he too roared with laughter as Weemullah snatched the glass while Maru glared over his shoulder.

Every man and woman snatched the glass until the *Ouida* seemed possessed by mad things whose roars and shrieks of laughter rolled out to the silent shore.

CHAPTER V

THE FLIGHT

THAT was a week of wonderful days—the Cahn-mah looting the *Ouida*. They stripped her to every bolt of iron then left her scarred, blood-stained decks to the sea and the wild sea birds. Back in their hidden camp again they lazed away the time, growing fat on the stolen food, smoking and smoking and smoking the good tobacco, fashioning wonderful spearheads and knives from the precious iron. By day, wispy smoke signals arising from Coor-i-ning and Coolandong look out told the tribes far and wide of the victory. Old Alligator and Maru loaded with spoils were ready to set out for the Fitzmaurice on the morrow, to tell Tiger details of the victory.

"Tell him," said Nemarluk fiercely, "that we can beat the white and Jap men. Tell him to be cunning. To make friends. Then when you are right amongst them kill them suddenly and they cannot use their guns." And the Red Band grunted assent.

"No need to tell Tiger be cunning," grinned Alligator.

"He is cunning as the snake," frowned Maru; "he will make his own plans. Come, we go. The people will be all waiting to hear us tell the news. It means the end of the white men."

And they vanished into the bush.

It was night and very quiet; just a whisper from the sea away back through the mangroves. Stars far above. All around Nemarluk's horde was the blackness of a dense vine scrub. The glow of their little fires was but the glow of coals deep down in hollowed shadows. The whites of eyes gleamed, now and then. Babies hardly whimpered. Every dog was quiet. The Australian aboriginal is always afraid of the dark. He believes that the spirits of the dead walk the earth when the sun has gone to sleep.

A night bird swished by on heavy wings. There came a croak of a nankin bird; it cackled harshly as it alighted on some distant tree. Marboo shivered.

"The crew boys who ran away!" she almost whimpered towards Nemarluk. "Won't they travel to the white man town Darwin and tell the police?"

"Bah!" he growled and showed his teeth. "They were frightened to death. They will be making haste back to their island. They won't dare go near the white men."

Nemarluk was right. The crew boys battled their way back to Melville Island and said nothing.

It was months later before the crew boys returned to Darwin. Then, fearing vengeance, they told a story of shipwreck, of how only themselves were saved. It was such a good story that even the owner of the vessel was satisfied she had gone down.

So the Red Band roamed the Wild Lands in untroubled triumph.

But Bul-bul got on the scent. He learned that Widjullee had killed white man Watts. And then a totem friend whispered: "Nemarluk's men have got guns!"

With a grin on his face Bul-bul reported to the little Daly River Police Station, and told his suspicions to Mounted-constable Pryor.

"It seems a long patrol," decided Pryor, and gave orders for the mustering of the police horses. He must run Widjullee to earth. Try to find out, too, something about that wild band towards the coast being in possession of guns.

The patrol vanished from the Daly.

And smoke signals rose up to warn those in the Wild Lands. Marboo came running into In-dar-roo camp: "Police!" she gasped. On their feet in an instant they ran to a vantage point. Then Nemarluk turned furiously on Marboo.

"It is only a smoke signal," he snarled. "The police are riding from the Daly into the Wild Lands. They are far away; they might not even be after us. Even if they are, they will never catch us."

"They might as well try to catch the eagle," laughed Mankee.

"Let us get back to the cooking fires," growled

Marragin. "If the white police do seek us we will know in good time."

But they did not know that another patrol had started out—Constable Don's patrol from Brock's Creek south of Darwin, another country altogether. Both patrols would work together to meet in surprising fashion right away out in the Wild Lands.

The surprise was all arranged for Widjullee.

Inland towards the ranges, the Cahn-mah now began burning off the long dry grass, wallaby hunting. Dense clouds of black smoke shot with flame rolled to the skies. A slow wind was driving the flames to encircle what had been a shallow swamp but was now a mass of dried water-plants and grasses. Among the sun-baked mounds under the big dried tufts, wallabies were sheltering. Two dingoes crouched there, too, their eyes reflecting the glare of the flames. From those encircling, creeping flames there was but one rapidly closing outlet and there the warriors were lined up hurling spears at the smoke-blinded animals as they came racing from the flames. A scorched snake bit deep into Wack-itchi's leg, and he screamed his fear when he saw it was red bellied. Clouds of brown hawks wheeled screeching overhead, diving down through the smoke to snatch marsupial mice and lizards and other small, terrified things.

The huntsmen now peering through the smoke threw fast as the terrified things bounded amongst them, yelling a warning too late as the two dingoes suddenly appeared and passed them like phantoms. Through the haze a throwing stick came hurtling and caught Bar-re-jar on the back of the neck. He fell like a stone. His woman screamed and leaped into the smoke and dragged him out by the heels.

It was a great hunt. When it was all over they

panted there, laughing down at twenty slain wallabies and a host of smaller game the women had killed with throwing sticks.

But a little apart, Wack-itchi crouched moaning. For very soon he must die. The scorched snake had pumped all its virulent poison into him in that last agonized bite.

After that hunt, and after they had put Wack-itchi in his last sleeping place, Mangul and Lin decided to visit Widjullee. He was a totem kinsmen and they knew his hideout in the ranges. It was only half a day's walk distant from the Valley of the Dead.

Mangul and Lin *did* visit Widjullee. And they were caught.

Dull coals were hidden by the squatting bodies of the killers. Weapons lay to hand ready for an instant dashaway. That was merely caution, because they felt quite secure. Danger was far away. Eight warriors squatted there, each with the band of the killer upon his brow. A little distance away in the darkness a few friendly tribesmen squatted, ears taking in the noises of the night. In low grunts the killers talked of raid and vendetta, of cattle spearing, and the spearing of men. Strong men and triumphant, all was well with the night. Presently, they coiled up and slept.

There came the first cold grey of dawn. The coals had died down, the bodies of the sleepers were coiled around the ashes. The sleep of the aboriginal towards dawn is a deep, heavy sleep. A bird twittered sleepily. Presently, a comrade answered it. A little later a bird twittered again, a little closer to the sleeping figures, it seemed.

Suddenly, a rush. Dim figures peering down at the sleepers then the "Click!" of steel on Widjullee's wrists.

A gloating "Ha! Ha!" and Mangul woke to fierce
hands upon him, the clasp of steel upon his wrists.
As Lin leaped up giant arms threw him back to the
ground as his wrist was jerked behind him: "Click!"
His other wrist was seized: "Click!"

"Ha! Ha! Ha!" laughed Bul-bul. He roared laughing, a deep bass roar while his eyes danced their delight.

"Who are these two?" demanded a stern voice.

"Mangul and Lin. Nemarluk's men!"

"Ah!"

The captives glared up at the stern white police, the
trackers around them. A real bird twittered this time,
chirped a happy awakening to the rising sun.

"What luck!" laughed Bul-bul in aboriginal langu-
age. "We come to visit Widjullee, and Widjullee has
visitors. Too bad! I know all about those guns at
Nemarluk's camp."

"When Nemarluk catches you," snarled Lin, "he
will kill you as he killed the Jap men!"

"Ah!" Then Bul-bul roared his laughter. The secret
was out.

It was not an hour later that Marboo suddenly called
out, pointing. From a peak away across in the ranges
a smoke signal rose lazily.

"Police!"

They stared at one another.

"They cannot be seeking us," said Nemarluk slowly.

Squatting there around the morning cooking fires
they stared at him, then across at the distant smoke.
The instinct of the wild knitted them so closely together that even the dogs sensed danger threatened.
The smoke faded, then a fresh column suddenly shot
straight up.

"Spears and food, quick!" ordered Nemarluk as he sprang up. "We go straight back to the coast."

The morning wore on. The horde made silent haste, the piccaninnies walking quietly with dogged look. By and by a runner came swiftly gaining upon them. They waited, staring back. With a speed and endurance possessed by no athlete in the world he was flying over the ground. Nor was he panting as he leaped among them.

"The white police!" he said to Nemarluk—"and Bulbul. Seeking you!"

Nemarluk nodded, his frowning eyes staring at the grim face of the runner.

"At dawn they caught Widjullee. Mangul and Lin too!"

"Ah!" exclaimed Nemarluk.

"Bul-bul swears he will catch you!"

Nemarluk threw his spears to the ground, stamping in uncontrollable rage. He shouted to the skies that he would kill Bul-bul; he swore it by his spirit totem The Red Band stared silently. Two of the band gone so suddenly, and not a blow struck!

"They put a chain upon their wrists," said the runner, "and took them away."

Nemarluk gazed up at the skies, there was an eagle sailing away up there, a free, happy eagle. Nemarluk gazed away over the bush towards the distant ranges. How calm they looked! he had glorified in their outline under rain and sun and wind and mist ever since his eyes could see. Close by a bird whistled shrilly, then sped happily away.

Lah-lee wailed softly. She was to have been the wife of Lin.

"They put steel upon their wrists," growled Nemarluk, "and took them away."

He glared wildly around. "They will never take me away!" he shouted. "Never! Never! Never!" Snatching up his spears he growled, "Come!"

The Red Band fell in behind him. Swiftly, quietly the tribe followed.

Nemarluk wheeled, heading straight back towards the ranges.

"Ha!" grunted Minmara.

"Bul-bul will take the police straight to the coast," growled Pooneemillar, "expecting we will be there."

"Wouldn't it be nice," said Mankee thoughtfully, "to feel your knife cutting out Bul-bul's kidney fat?"

"Wah! Wah! Wah!" they agreed.

Nemarluk led them straight to the big swamps. They took to the water for the remainder of the day, wading for miles. Across this portion of the plains he led them by way of lagoon and swamp. In waterhole after water-hole he made them lose their tracks again and again. That night he camped them upon an island in the heart of a swamp. He allowed no fires. All slept huddled together for warmth, piccaninnies and dogs, deep in among the reeds, with an occasional splash of water, the boom of a heron, the shrill cackle of a nankin bird as their slumber song.

In the chill of dawn they were wading again, and every slimy log underfoot felt like a crocodile. When they came to the ranges Nemarluk's tall form strode on into the deepest, rockiest gorge. He frowned upon his followers, making them walk the rocks—men, women, and serious-faced, scared children. Two days later the tribe was walled in by cliffs far above which was a blue line of sky, and finally reached a canyon where were many caves, some the burial places of this most ancient of people. On many a ledge here were the skulls of their fathers and fathers' fathers, and

D

beetle-eaten old bones and little heaps of dirty greyish powder that were the last of men who had lived long ago. Deep down here in this gloomy canyon, in this, their Valley of the Dead, the walls were split by deep, narrow cracks that led far into cliff and mountain. Deep into these cliffs hunted men could disappear like startled wallabies. A sighing waterfall gave water to this tribal hideout of the Cahn-mah.

To-morrow in this heart of unnamed ranges Nemarluk's horde would split up into sub-hordes; the day after into tribal groups. Thus they would spread out over many miles of the ranges. If the chase became hot, or if food became scarce the groups would split again into family groups. Thus, even if tracked, the police would never surprise the tribe. And thus, from many a mountain look out some members of the Cahn-mah would be watching over many miles.

That night, the horde held council.

"It is good," declared the old Inkata, "we have not left track of even dog upon plain or ridge or rock. By now, the white police will be seeking us towards the coast. They will seek until their cursed feet grow weary but all they will find will be our burnt-out fires."

"And then?" questioned Mankee.

"We hide in safety until the big rains come. Then the police must ride away otherwise their animals will bog."

"Why not leave the women here," growled Marragin, "and rescue Mangul and Lin?"

"I've thought of that," snapped Nemarluk. "We must make the tribe safe first then find out what numbers the police are. Our watchers on the hills have failed us. While they watched one patrol, another has come another way."

"They've travelled by night," said Mankee, "over country where no hunters would see their tracks. Where have they come from?"

"Ask the eagle," growled Pooneemillar.

"To-morrow, the horde separate into their totem hordes," declared Nemarluk. "Look after my people!" he ordered as he glared at the Red Band and the warriors around them. "Mankee alone will stay by me, unless I signal." He frowned at the coals, thinking. Silently they stared towards the big chief. Marboo shivered, but not with cold, although it was cold down there in the pitch-black canyon. Their fires were glowing coals, hidden among the rocks. The green eyes of the dogs flamed again and again as they stared suspiciously around. Huge black rocks seemed to be polished red as they reflected light from the coals.

"The police will raid our An-de-mallee camp," frowned Nemarluk. "They will raid In-dar-roo. Only the ghosts of the Jap men will be there. They will raid all our coastal camps, our swamp camps, our hunting camps. Then, they will ride far away down to the Victoria River, where the white men's cattle stations are. They will raid the camps along the river, thinking we will visit the people there, to trade for tobacco. But we won't be there. They will take much time in looking for us in the places they must look, in the places they don't know, and travel, travel, travel. And when they travel our people everywhere will signal us where they are. If ever in danger, make straight for where the police have last camped."

Nemarluk was right. Even while they sat planning, a patrol was hastening towards An-de-mallee camp. Bul-bul was leading the way, riding clear of all places where an ambush might be in wait.

Well he knew how the tribesmen would love to sink a spear between his ribs. He laughed softly to himself, his big eyes glowing. This was the man hunt he loved —the hunt for Nemarluk.

Several days later Bul-bul, away on the coast, found the body of Nagata. An unpleasant job judging by the face of the young policeman. But the hunt had given Bul-bul the keenest delight; his big face deadly earnest then breaking into smiles as step by step, yard by yard, mile by mile he unravelled the evidence of this deed committed so many months ago.

That patrol proved the killing. Now it remained to catch the actual killers.

"We have made a good beginning," wrote the policeman in his diary that night. "We've arrested Mangul and Lin. But Nemarluk the chief is going to prove very difficult to run to earth."

Meanwhile, nearly two hundred miles south another patrol was craftily encircling a Victoria River camp. But the raid brought them nothing except the quiet jeers of the natives.

Weeks slipped into months. Then Nemarluk made a shrewd move. With Mankee, Coon-an-pore, Me-al-cull and a few others of his people, he came down on to the plains and made straight for the Victoria River. The patrols were now in the bush, hopelessly seeking him. Nemarluk slipped behind them and, laughing, kept travelling away from them, along the very country over which they had just ridden. He turned at a grunt from Mankee. Far away, from a peak towards the head of the Fitzmaurice River, a thin smoke signal rose lazily. As they watched it, a puff shot up; then the column rose again. Another puff shot up forming a wee, vanishing cloud. Then the column rose again, blacker smoke this time.

"Alligator," grunted Mankee, "signals police travelling towards Did-ee plain."

Nemarluk laughed, then turned to walk on. But with a wild shriek Marboo flung herself at his feet. Nemarluk leaped as if a snake had bitten him, and whirled around with poised spear. Mankee had also turned, his spear searching for the patrol. With beating hearts both glared at Marboo. She had leaped up and was standing trembling, eyes staring from her head, finger pointing.

Nemarluk frowned. Wriggling away from where his foot would have trod was a red-bellied snake. At that season of the year a bite from that reptile means death in three minutes.

To Nemarluk's glance Marboo shook her head. No, it had not bitten her. Everything happened so suddenly that the snake had been too startled to strike.

Nemarluk killed the snake and strode on.

CHAPTER VI

DEVEN'S COUNTRY

The little band came now into cattle country, luxuriantly grassed plains hedged by rugged ranges in the distance. Nemarluk vanished down a dry creek, the others following. In a little while Nemarluk glanced back, with a grimace of caution. Mankee was instantly beside him.

They peered up over the bank and there, not two hundred yards away, was grazing a little mob of cattle. With a silent laugh and a glitter in their eyes the two powerful bodies crawled up into the grass and wormed their way towards the cattle. It was a windless day, they got right in amongst them before an old bull lifted his head and sniffed uneasily. Instantly the spearmen arose and two shovel-bladed spears shot towards a fat young steer. It plunged and wheeled completely around to bellow and gallop madly away. But only for two hundred yards. The bladed spearheads had ripped deep into and right up his body, he bled to death as he galloped. Terrible cutting things, are those shovel-bladed spears.

Nemarluk's people enjoyed a hurried feast, eating only the titbits.

"There are plenty more cattle," laughed Coon-an-pore; "and now we are at war with the whites it doesn't matter how many we kill."

"Kill as many as we can," growled Me-al-cull.

"My spear is going to kill and kill and kill," boasted Mankee.

"No," frowned Nemarluk. "Don't kill when the

police are close on your tracks. Kill as many as you like otherwise."

They walked on cheerily, eyes keenly roving ahead and around, and watching the ground for tracks as they walked. No hunters had been over this country for some time nor was there any sign of station blacks. They walked cautiously, now, speculating on what friends might be present in the native camp at the station, and what tribal enemies might be there also. Eagerly they debated their chances of cajoling or demanding tobacco from the station boys. The ranges before them now appeared as great brown walls, the frowning ramparts of Bradshaw's Lookout standing up plainly. Those ranges were on the other side of the river, as were the most of the half-dozen widely scattered homesteads.

And now Nemarluk made cunning plans. For the time being at least he alone would cross the river. First to quietly meet a band of wild renegades there; then to terrorize, if need be, the station boys. The police were far away behind them searching in the opposite direction. If they doubled back, Nemarluk's people would warn him. To catch him, the police must cross the river. Nemarluk would wait for them to cross; then he would cross back again and be away, travelling straight back into his own country.

The strategy was sound. For to cross that broad, very dangerous river, with horses, meant that a patrol must travel up from the river mouth nearly a hundred miles to the crossing. Then down the other side of the river.

"And when they do come," grinned Nemarluk, "I'll cross the river and they'll have to go all the way back again."

"And if the police don't come, or if they come too soon?" inquired Coon-an-pore.

"Then you and the others except two can cross and join me. I'll send word as soon as I'm sure we can boss the station boys. But two must always stay on this side of the river."

"If only I could see Bul-bul," grunted Mankee—and felt the edge of his spear.

"Be certain that you see him first," laughed Nemarluk, "or we'll have to bury you."

Into the afternoon Nemarluk strode on alone. The others turned towards a group of hills. Presently, from a peak there rose a smoke signal. Miles away across the river a watcher on Bradshaw's Lookout saw the signal; read the sign. Lazily he picked up his spears and vanished amongst the rocks.

Night, with a little moon. Stars, in a sky of velvet. Trees, and the smell of water. And then—the sound of water, the murmuring, hissing, lapping of angry waters. Otherwise silence. Then the murmuring of the waters growing louder while a keen ear could hear distantly a vagrant breeze rustle over dry grass. Now the hoarse, rasping cry of the night heron. Silence again, with the slight "feeling" of noise whispering over great distances across vast spaces.

Then there rose to the skies the long-drawn, shuddering howl of a dingo, the howl of an old-man dog calling his pack to the chase. After that howl had moaned away it still seemed to ring over plain, and gorge, and river. And then—silence.

"Wow-wow!" "Wow-wow!" came the hoot of a boobook owl.

From where the dingo had howled rose a shadow, which strode forward noiselessly.

In among the black river trees where the boobook owl had called was blackness. And a man black as the night, awaited the shadow's coming. They met. Their eyes gleamed.

"So! Nemarluk comes."

"And Deven greets him!"

Their voices were but the murmuring of the night.

"Where land and waters meet, where the mountains reach towards the skies there shall our people ever be."

"By the river of our fathers we pledge our word," answered Nemarluk.

They stared into one another's eyes, spears upright in each left hand. Then each reached his right hand to the other's shoulder, their foreheads gently touched. Then Deven stepped into a canoe. Nemarluk stepped in beside him but stood, a spear ready gripped, his fierce eyes glancing to right and left searching the water. The canoe shot out from the blackness of the trees.

At that spot the river is a mile wide, fierce currents rush up from the sea. In Whirlpool Pass the waters rage and whine threatening to engulf anything within reach of their whirling arms. The tide was rushing out now with an angry murmuring that possessed the night. Away across the tortured water loomed a black wall of mountains.

The canoe shot ahead as Deven paddled. Starlight shone on his muscled body and seemed to kiss this child of her own. Powerful, fiercely cunning, relentless in his loves and hates and feuds was and is—Deven. Scourge of the whites, he had been hunted by blacks and whites alike. He at last had cowed the blacks. In his triumph and ignorance he thought he would be for ever free. But—the whites once had caught him.

Far away into the white man's jail at Darwin they threw this untamed child of the wilds. He escaped.

Fought his way back to his own country; took quick revenge on those who had betrayed him; swore he would never be caught again. He never has been!

A hoarse grunt, a low bellow as of a bull struggling upon the water, then a mighty splash. Coughings, gaspings, hoarse roars as two bull alligators fought. The canoe sped on.

Presently, a dull black snout rose beside the canoe, effortlessly followed it. Nemarluk snarled noiselessly. The snout appeared astern. Yet another snout rose beside it, and another appeared ahead. Merciless eyes glared at the primitives in the tiny canoe. Terrible things, these estuarine crocodiles of the north. Nemarluk threatened his spear towards each in turn.

He hated but loved these fierce things, things as wild and free as himself. They fought to live. He fought to live. And all the world—their world—was theirs.

They crossed in safety. Deven hid the canoe.

"Tiger has sent word," murmured Deven fiercely, "two white men are away up at the crossing. They are fitting out; going to travel through Tiger's country, through the Fitzmaurice. They seek the yellow stone they call gold. Tiger watches them. His men await him away back on the Fitzmaurice. When the men reach that country then Tiger is going to fall upon them. He will kill them."

"He carries on the war," answered Nemarluk grimly.

"We all do—all but the station mongrels. They fear for their lives. Any one of them who breathes a word to white man or police will die—and they know it."

"And the camps away up, and away down the river?" questioned Nemarluk.

"Are all afraid of Deven's men. My totem brothers are everywhere, and yet they never know who they may be. But let a man whisper against us and very soon I will know."

"And then?" grinned Nemarluk. Silence was Deven's reply. Nemarluk chuckled. "One day," he said reminiscently, "I met two hunted men far back in Talakinyin Gorge. They answered as you do."

Still Deven was silent.

"Their tongues had been cut out," murmured Nemarluk.

"Come!" said Deven.

They walked on, shadows across a plain with the black wall before them. They were in Legune station country now. A mile farther on they halted.

Deven drew back his head, and in perfect imitation went out "Wow-wow! Wow-wow!" the call of the boobook owl.

Presently, the whistle of a whistling duck came in answer. The two shadows moved on and stepped into the bush blacks' camp.

Glaring eyes by dull coals. Warriors' eyes, womens' eyes, childrens' eyes, dogs' eyes. And the sullen eyes of the station blacks.

All stared at Nemarluk. Then the bush blacks laughed eagerly and greeted him as the hero.

Pooneemillar glared up from his fire, his woman beside him. His fierce face rarely smiled; now it seemed to shine. He adored Nemarluk. Near by was the giant Kerinbo, with massive chest and shoulders, and the voice of a bull. His hairy face spread into one great smile of welcome. These were two of the most cunning cattle spearers in the Territory, the whites on many a station would have given a lot to lay them by the heels.

Kummungeegut stood up; his big eyes deep set in

a handsome fierce face smiled greeting. A giant athlete this. One who had attacked the lugger *Pat*. As elusive as a night bird this raider, lithe as a panther, as graceful as any man could be, but ferocious as the tiger. With a cunning matched only by his fearlessness he never yet had been caught for any misdeed. He welcomed Nemarluk to this band of free, wild men. Others glared, then grunted a greeting. All savage men these, quick with spear and knife.

And around them, glaring silently, squatted the Legune station boys. Many of them secretly admired Nemarluk but feared Deven and his wild band; feared and envied them because they were game to defy the whites while they had taken to the softer life of tame station blacks.

"Should police appear away on the other side of the river," sneered Deven, "your people there and the others of the river tribes will let us know. Should police appear on this side away up at the crossing then word will speed down to us fast. Every man who works for a station will send us word or signal. They know that our warriors will kill any who do not. Now we eat."

For weeks Nemarluk with Deven's band raided the station cattle, those vast, unfenced stations with their lonely people, their tiny homesteads so many miles apart. And, very uneasily, the station stockboys wisely held their tongues.

One morning Deven took Nemarluk far up to his favourite look out. Standing there like eagles they gazed out across the Victoria River, far away toward Nemarluk's beloved country. To their right and left for mile upon mile swept ramparts of cliffs, changing from brown to red and purple as clouds drifted across the sun. In behind them, was Deven's country, a maze of ranges. Within those canyons, those labyrinths of gorge and hideout he could disappear and would never be taken.

There rose up the grim ramparts of Bradshaw's Lookout. High up there, overlooking the station he pioneered, sleeps Bradshaw, speared by the natives years ago. Bradshaw loved this country. But so did Nemarluk, staring out over his own, his very own, country. Far below them like a vast stream of silver swept the twisting river to the sea, hedged in by its squat boab trees, its snow white paper-barks, its clumps of scrub and jungle; by its fertile plains and purple tinted mountains. Far over the river spread the haze of other plains and mountains, Nemarluk's plains and mountains. His eyes grew misty as he stared.

"Come," said Deven. Down a crag upon which a goat could hardly walk he took Nemarluk back into his own ranges, Deven's ranges. From among the tangled vines of a ravine a skeleton stared up at them.

"That is why the station stockboys are afraid to put us away to the police," said Deven grimly. "I found that though a man has no tongue he can still talk with his fingers. Come!"

Among fallen boulders they worked their way up a gloomy ravine. Here, like a stricken dingo had crawled another into a cave, to die.

"He too," said Deven grimly, "wagged his tongue to the white police trackers."

"If we could only get Bul-bul here!" hissed Nemarluk.

"He knows too much," answered Deven. "But we will get him some night—on the plains."

A week later, away across the river, a smoke signal shot up.

"Police!"

Nemarluk stared at Deven.

"So the white dogs come," sneered Deven.

"It is the black dogs we must watch!" snarled Nemarluk.

CHAPTER VII

POLICE!

Next day the people on the opposite side canoed lazily across the river. And great were the laughs at the expense of the white police at night when the look out men came down from the mountains. For they told of what they saw, and of the weary, unavailing search of those on the opposite bank.

At the camp fire, council was held among the wild men. Spears to hand, suspicious glances out towards the night where Marboo and her friends lay watching, all eyes, all ears, hidden to the earth in the darkness of night. Sudden death now to any station stockboy listening-in to the council of the wild men.

"We will kill them!" hissed Nemarluk. And he meant the white police.

"Not here," cautioned Deven, "where the white men on the stations are their friends. Lure them far into your own country, into Tiger's country where there are no white men, no tame natives, no black spies. We will call together your Red Band, Tiger's Mob, and my men. Let them chase you first. Lure them deep into the ranges in Tiger's country where Chugulla's men are strong. Then, all together, we will fall upon them."

"It is a good plan," hissed Kummungeegut. "We will kill them all. Every policeman, every tracker, every horse."

"Look out you don't miss again!" hissed Poonee-millar. The hairy giant Kerinbo bellowed with laughter. They stopped him instantly, glaring out into the night as Deven sprang at Kummungeegut who was struggling for Pooneemillar's throat.

"Fools!" snarled Deven. "Do you want to bring the trackers upon us?"

"No man sneers at me!" hissed Kummungeegut.

"It is good advice, not a sneer!" snarled Deven.

"That fool Wa-gar was so anxious, he bumped my arm as I swung the tomahawk!" hissed Kummungeegut, "otherwise I would have split the policeman's skull instead of his fingers!"

"We know," said Deven. "But don't miss again. You won't be attacking a lugger next time with the crew asleep. We'll attack a wide-awake patrol armed with many guns. Keep quiet. Listen!"

But there came no sound, other than the sounds of the night.

"They will search the other side of the river for days," declared Deven at last. "Their horses are all there, so they could not have crossed. Only Bul-bul might have crossed alone."

"If only he would come!" hissed Nemarluk.

"He would never walk into the little traps we have here," declared Deven. "It will take a clever trap to catch Bul-bul."

"I'm not clever," said Kerinbo in a hoarse whisper, "but if only I could catch him in these." And he held out mighty arms.

"You'd wake up with his dagger in your belly," said Deven contemptuously. "Now let us plan so that we can kill them all while they can kill none of us."

Their tense faces leaned over the camp fire coals, their eyes gleamed, their faces changed as the tigress's changes as she plays with, then snarls over, her cubs.

This was their country; they would fight against the white man's law.

But it was only Deven who fully realized they must fight with cunning. He had once been like these, wild and free in his own country, laughing at the very thought that the white police could ever catch him. But he had been outmatched; had felt the weight of the law; had been caged in a jail; had seen a white man town. He knew far more of the power of the whites than his wild tribesmen. He knew that to lure away, then ambush and kill, every member of a fighting patrol was going to need far more than premature cunning and daring.

He ordered his henchmen to spread word up and down the river that he had redoubled his threat to cut to pieces any native who gave hint or whisper to white police, trackers, or white man.

Deven and Nemarluk now retired to the cliffs. The others remained in camp, Deven's men maliciously watching the stockboys, joining with Nemarluk's handful of warriors in spearing the white men's cattle and in generally making a nuisance of themselves. Plenty of time for Nemarluk's people to move, after the white police across the river proved their search unavailing and started out on the weary ride up river to the crossing. Only when they had to ride all the way down this side would Nemarluk's people cross the river and dawdle back to their own country.

One dark night among the rocks, two black shadows squatted by the glowing embers of a fire. A terrible shriek rang up the gorge. Wild things in caves, in trees, in crannies of the rock, trembled. But Deven threw back his head and "Wow-wow! Wow-wow!" hooted the boobook owl.

Presently, a shadow stepped from among the rocks,

E

and Kummungeegut squatted smiling beside them.

"The white police search and search and search. They have ridden away but we have no real news where yet. Nemarluk's people have crossed the river now. We watch the stockboys, but they daren't speak."

"Good reason or why," sneered Deven. "There has been no canoe left across the river?"

"Not one."

"And no word yet from up river?"

"No word. The people there will signal immediately the police cross."

"And I will wait until they are but a few hours away," said Nemarluk grimly. "I'll leave my tracks plain across the river. I'll lure them far away back into the mountains, to where my Red Band wait."

"Tiger's Mob will be waiting too," snarled Deven, "and—we will follow up behind."

Only a few nights later, as Nemarluk sat staring into the coals, a shadow stepped beside him. He glanced up at Deven's furious face.

"Police!" snarled Deven.

Nemarluk sprang up and his spears threatened the night.

"Not here," hissed Deven. "Down in the Legune camp. They have got Pooneemillar and Kerinbo, Kummungeegut and Mankee."

"Mankee!" exclaimed Nemarluk, "Kummungeegut! Pooneemillar! Kerinbo!" He stared as if at a ghost.

"Yes," snarled Deven. "Caught one by one as they strolled into camp from the hunt. They were hidden in the camp. They made the people go about their ordinary work, even made them play the didjeridoo and sing when sundown came. One policeman was hidden there, and all the trackers. One by one our men came into the cooking fires. The police snatched at

their very feet—they almost caught mine!" Deven's
eyes rolled, his strong teeth gritted. Nemarluk stared
at him.

"Kummungeegut was walking ahead," snarled
Deven, "fifty steps ahead. It was dark; the camp fires
were burning. We could see the people squatting around
them; the women were roasting kangaroo and snakes.
There was one snake there I'll roast myself!" he snarled.
"We saw Sandy pick up his didjeridoo; some people
started to corroboree. Then Kummungeegut screamed
his signal call. A snake of a hag screamed reply and
Kummungeegut walked into the trap. Straight to the
fire, threw down his spears, and the policeman was
upon him. Kummungeegut snatched at his spears but
the policeman stunned him with his gun. I flung myself flat in the dark.

"Presently I rose up. I could partly see then one big
policeman, big as you, crouching beside our men. And
each man had steel upon his wrists. The barrel of a
gun poked from a bush a little distance away. I saw
the eyes of Splinter the tracker. I did not know which
others might be close around me; to spear the policeman I would have had to jump up—I had no chance.
Presently, Kummungeegut sat up, staring around as
if an alligator had swallowed him. Kerinbo laughed
like a bull, squatting there with steel upon his wrists.
When they had tripped him up he had been too silly
to fight; he just lay there gazing while they snapped
the steal on. Then he knew what had happened. He
looked at the steel—and laughed. He thinks it funny.
But when he is walking day after day to jail, he will
not think it so humorous."

Deven paused, frowning. "Then the policeman asked
Kummungeegut where you were," he went on. "Kummungeegut showed his teeth and spat, then sneered

at him. The policeman grew angry but Kummungee-gut laughed again, 'Ask the winds!' he mocked, 'ask the winds and the night bird and the owl in the mountains.' And he laughed again."

"That woman who decoyed Kummungeegut into the trap?" said Nemarluk softly.

"I saw Marboo's eyes when the woman screeched," answered Deven grimly.

"Marboo!" exclaimed the startled Nemarluk.

"Yes, they caught her too."

The boyishness vanished from Nemarluk's face.

"I thought the police were still on the other side of the river," he said harshly.

"So they are—or one is, the one our men have been watching. But the other crossed the river—somehow. He did not cross away up at the crossing, he crossed here, without horses—somehow. He must have been hiding on this side all the time we have been watching the other."

"Come," hissed Nemarluk, "we will spear him."

Deven laughed softly. "That is the talk I like," he whispered. Grasping their spears they crept down on to the plain and felt the cool breath from the river.

Black night and silence except for the hoarse blast of a distant didjeridoo. They stepped as softly as shadows of the night, but their eyes watchful as wild animals' eyes; their nostrils breathing in the scents of the night, their ears catching sounds that white men never would notice. Suddenly, they halted. Not a sound—but there *was* a sound, and they had heard it. Like the soft breathing of an animal some distance away. The bare feet of softly running men. They stared into the night, heads slowly turning as the ear traced the sound. Barefooted men running out to the side of them to circle around, facing them.

They stared at one another knowing now that a line of men was spread out ahead of them, lying down now, awaiting them.

Deven turned and with swift, noiseless strides headed down river. Nemarluk followed. When a few hundred yards away, they broke into a swift run that ended at the river. Leaping into a canoe they swiftly paddled outstream.

"They'll follow our tracks at daylight," hissed Deven. "They'll think you've crossed the river—perhaps."

"Perhaps," growled Nemarluk. "They are clever."

In midstream a strong tide caught the canoe. Deven swung her nose around and she sped downstream like a living thing.

Around them a hissing swirl of waters, far above them the stars with distantly to left and right black shadows of trees. Far away those shadows receded as towards dawn they neared Blunder Bay, the river mouth. Before them loomed up the black mass of Timber Island. With deft strokes Deven paddled the canoe to the island. Nemarluk leaped ashore.

"I'll hide the canoe and walk back along the foot-hills," said Deven. "They'll find no tracks to follow now. I'll send up a smoke when the other policeman crosses over to this side. Then you cross the river and make your getaway. When the police have left the Victoria I'll send you word. You double back but bring your Red Band and we'll deal with the station stock-boys, some might be cheeky now that the police have got our good men. I'll send word to Tiger to bring his mob and meet us here. Then we can all plan what we'll do."

"Yu ai!" grunted Nemarluk.

"Watch for my signals!" warned Deven, and pushed off.

Next day Nemarluk watched the river, stared towards the distant cliffs upstream for a smoke signal, speared fish for food, idly watched the snouts of cruising crocodiles. Darkness came with the tide swirling in, a hissing and a moaning from the whirlpools in Whirlpool Pass. Feeling very lonely Nemarluk sat there by the island edge spear in hand, staring upstream. To his ears came the sounds of the night, the moaning of tortured waters, the cough of a bull alligator. The weird, rasping call of the grey night bird, the soft rustle of passing wings.

To his nostrils came the smells of the night, spume air from violent mixture of sea and fresh water, smell of trees, whiff from some distant mud flat being disturbed by the tide. Nemarluk watched, Nemarluk chief of the wilds, Nemarluk the hunter, Nemarluk the hunted.

Suddenly a star appeared. Far distant, up in the black sky. A red star.

Nemarluk sprang up, trembling. That star was Deven's signal fire.

"Police!"

So, they had guessed his hideout—were coming now! He gazed at the stars; his fine chest filled out. There, all alone, he snarled defiance.

He hurried across to the opposite side of the island, where there were two dead logs of a light wood he had noted that morning. Near by grew a long jungle creeper, its stem strong as knotted cord. Swiftly he pulled the creeper, fastened the two logs together, and collected a score of heavy sticks. He launched the logs, lay flat upon them with the sticks resting before him, his spears under him, and pushed out into the night.

The current urged the logs out and upstream. With a tough piece of bark he steered, allowing the tide to sweep the logs along. At a long slant he was bound for the opposite shore. Snappy little waves leaped from darkness and slapped the raft. White scum appeared only to whirl by into the night. The black fin of a shark swept swiftly upstream.

Nemarluk had travelled a full half mile before the first black snout appeared, wicked little eyes peering from out deep sockets. The thing surged forward. Nemarluk grasped a stick, skilfully and sideways he threw. The thing disappeared, vanished easily with incredible swiftness before the stick touched the water.

Presently another snout appeared, then another, and swam with him, waiting their chance. Not true alligators these but the estuarine crocodile; bigger, stronger, more cunning, faster and fiercer than any alligator. But our bushmen have always called these terrors the "alligator".

An old bull appeared. Craftily he surveyed the speeding logs; swam beside them, but a little distance away. Just the knobs of his snout, the ridges around his eyes, his long, serrated tail, were visible.

Nemarluk, guiding the logs, watched intently. This one was the danger. He dashed a stick towards it but the thing took no notice.

Nemarluk grasped a spear. How he hated losing one of his beloved spears! The logs sped on. The man waited. The alligator waited. All sped on into the night.

CHAPTER VIII

HUNTED MAN

SUDDENLY the alligator surged forward. Nemarluk's spear arm flashed out, and the blade bit deep into the alligator right across the horny ridges of the eye. With a terrific splash it disappeared. Presently the others reappeared a little away. But the old bull never came back.

The logs sped on while the man's fierce eyes swept to right and left. Those logs bobbed violently as they skimmed the rims of whirlpools. One opened out ahead and Nemarluk steered tensely to avoid it, his eyes seeing in the night, his ears tuned to the changing hissings in the waters, his body feeling through the logs every vibration of current, tide, and whirlpool. The black mass of the shore appeared ahead.

Nemarluk leaped ashore and sped on, keeping to the salt arms of the estuary, to the many boggy places where horses could not follow. He travelled thus for twenty miles then came out on hard country and sped on, neither stopping to hunt nor eat. In less than twenty-four hours he put one hundred miles between him and the river. Then he slept, hidden deep within a great saltpan. And the "swish—swash—swee-ass-oosh" of the tide on the mangrove roots was his lullaby.

Nemarluk awoke in a daylight gloom among a tangle of roots with dense foliage overhead. He listened, peering cautiously among the roots at grey-white expanses of saltpan. A hoarse croaking drew his eyes to a maze of fallen trees, black with cormorants. By the metallic sheen on their coats he knew that "outside" the sun must be shining brightly. Cautiously he made his way inland through the mangroves and came out on to open forest country. There he climbed a dwarf scrub-tree on a hillock and gazed away back. Far distant was a haze of smoke that told of hunters burning off the grass. But no sign of human life elsewhere. His eye swept the sky watching the flight of birds. They were flying naturally, unalarmed. Relieved, he hurried on, the hunger light in his eyes. He saw tiny tracks of the night before and followed them to a cosy, grass-lined tunnel; reached in his arm and grasped a sleeping bandicoot. In a forest of beautiful eucalyptus-trees his sharp eyes saw tell-tale scratches around a hollow limb, high up. He flung his hands around the tree, gripped it with his feet and "walked" up. Reaching into the hollow he roughly woke a little flying phalanger, a pretty fellow with a bluish-grey coat.

Later Nemarluk stopped at a small lagoon around which grew squat nutmeg-trees. He hurried to a fallen tree and from its very light, very dry wood selected two sticks. Near by, two huge paper-barks grew close together, and between them was a tiny, grassy hollow. Here he rubbed a handful of dry grass into shreds, and placing his sticks amongst the shreds rubbed them swiftly together. Within a minute a wisp of smoke arose, a spark shot out, the fluffy grass caught alight. Nemarluk threw on a handful of teased bark, then tinder and had his fire. He hardly waited for coals. Throwing his game on the fire he turned it over as the fur singed; then tore it to pieces with his strong teeth and wolfed it. Feeling much better he picked up his spears, and walked on, travelling parallel with the coast. Within a few miles the forest gave way to a wide area of tufted grasses that covered the earth like a dense mat.

Now, for the first time, Nemarluk sought to hide his tracks. He was travelling east. Suddenly, he turned directly south and no longer walked upon the grass but *under* it. With extreme care he would stretch out a leg and gently insert his foot under a tuft where the long grass had drooped from the root to the earth. Then he would stretch out the other leg and step similarly, carefully withdrawing a foot to step forward again. As he lifted his foot the hardly disturbed grass dropped back into place. So he walked for miles, and never once did he set his foot upon grass.

And for a very good reason. Not only can the aboriginal follow tracks upon earth, the clever ones among them can detect the faint imprint of a foot upon grass also—whether the grass be green and moist with early morning dew, or brown and dry. He who might be on Nemarluk's tracks would have his work cut out now. Horses could not follow him that hundred tortuous miles across saltpan and bog and mangrove. The horses would have to travel miles away out along the edge of the hard country while the trackers laboriously tracked him often deep within mangrove labyrinths. And now that he was in open forest he had completely altered direction and was travelling "under" grass. Even if they detected the trick the trackers would have to carefully examine thousands of tufts of grass, carefully lift up the grass, and then search for trace of the imprint upon the hard earth underneath. For mile upon mile the tracker must slowly search under tuft after countless tuft. If he completely lost the track, he would ride in a semi-circle, covering miles, seeking to cut the tracks where they came out of this tufted area of grass country.

But Nemarluk had thought of this. Next day, still taking his time, he was leisurely wading a creek. It was dark and cool for the banks on each side were dense walls of jungle vine. Nemarluk was wading upstream and meant to keep on for the creek headed in the mountains of Tiger's country. He meant to talk with Tiger and Chugulla; to have their tribesmen signal his Red Band come and meet him; then signal Deven and try and arrange a rescue for Mankee and Kerinbo, Kummungeegut, Pooneemillar, Kin Aerry, Marboo and all who had been captured by that patrol. Nemarluk was making no tracks at all now for the quiet water swallowed every track he made. Neither Bul-bul nor any tracker born could now follow him.

Suddenly a scrub wallaby hopped out of the vines on the right bank and stood erect, nostrils and ears twitching, listening with its back towards the man. He stood motionless, tensely alert. . . . The sound of men! The wallaby vanished as Nemarluk leaped for the bank. But it was only Wambun and Widgee, greatly excited. They pushed through the vines, their eyes vivid under circles of war paint, then stared in amazement.

"Nemarluk!" they shouted.

"Wah!" grinned Nemarluk.

They plunged across the stream to him, greatly excited.

"We all thought you were hurrying back towards Ande-miller camp," exclaimed Wambun. "We have great news."

"What is it?"

"Tiger's Mob have killed the two white men!"

Nemarluk stared.

"The two white men Tiger was watching up at the crossing while you were down river with Deven," exclaimed Widgee.

"Ah!"

Then they told him all about it. The two lonely wanderers setting out on their last voyage, down the broad river, along the wild coast, then into the mouth of the gloomy Fitzmaurice, far from white men or aid. Tiger hurrying back through the bush, collecting Chugulla and his mob, then trailing the wanderers far up river into the Little Fitzmaurice.

Painted figures, unseen figures, watching them all the time.

A day came when the white men stepped ashore far up in the heart of the primitives' land. Carrying their prospecting tools, with revolvers at their belts, they ventured a little distance inland.

And Tiger's Mob fell upon them.

Tiger and Chugulla, Wadawarry and Walung, Alligator and Maru and the rest of Tiger's Mob. They cut the two men to pieces; just a writhing, snarling, hacking fight in the loneliness of the Wild Lands.

Nemarluk laughed in delight. So the war was on in earnest, he was not fighting alone.

"We will wipe out the white men!" he declared fiercely.

"Wah!" exclaimed Wambun.

"Wah!" echoed Widgee.

Eagerly they talked. The two messengers had seen no patrol; every smoke signal over many miles was "All Clear". They were hurrying now to the Daly to tell the tribesmen there.

"If only we could wipe out the settlement on the Daly!" said Nemarluk thoughtfully.

Wambun's eyes widened, Widgee's eyes widened. Wipe out a settlement! The idea was too big for them to grasp just yet.

"We will talk of it later," said Nemarluk shortly,

"when Deven and Tiger and Chugulla and I hold council."

The messengers explained that Tiger's Mob had doubled back towards the Victoria. Only the black men would ever know what had happened to the white men, the police would never know for crocodiles had long since dined on the two bodies. Tiger had not left a trace.

They parted with a "Ma-muck!" "Ma-muck!" the messengers hurrying on. Nemarluk now left the creek for Tiger would not be up on the mountains. Nemarluk decided to double back to the Victoria. He would meet Tiger and Deven there, and they would talk. He hurried out on to the open forest country and glanced towards the distant ranges. From a look out a smoke signal was rising, telling of the killing of a warrior by a vengeance band. But there was no signal that warned of a patrol, the police must be far away. Nemarluk hurried on, thinking of Tiger's success. Throughout all the Wild Lands the news would fly on the wings of the wind. The killing of the Jap men, and now the killing of the white men. Every warrior would be eager for more victories; every timid one would become brave.

"Deven and Tiger and I will get together," whispered Nemarluk fiercely, "and kill all the white men, even the police patrol." He gritted his teeth, clenching his spears. He was walking with long, swinging strides. Suddenly he halted, staring at the ground. A footprint, a big, plain footprint upon a soft patch of soil!

"Police!"

Nemarluk knew it. The footprint of a white man.

Nemarluk glared wildly around. Nothing moved; there was not a sound. He stared at the track again.

There was only the one man, the one track going towards the east. A fresh track, not an hour old. If

Nemarluk had not left the creek the man who made
that track and he would have just about met at the
creek.

Nemarluk panicked; turned and headed straight
back for the coast—running. He must put distance between him and that track.

He was a hunted man. At last he realized it. They
were after him—were hunting Nemarluk.

Those look out people away back on the ranges—
they had not seen him. Wambun and Widgee knew
nothing of them. No one had seen them. But here they
were—around him—near him—somewhere.

He expected the thud of galloping hooves, expected
a loud challenge, a rifle shot, and the whistle of a bullet.
He expected—anything.

But there was only silence. He turned again towards
the ranges intent on deceiving the pursuers by doubling
back through a swamp. As he hurried on, his thoughts
were grim.

The Red Band scattered; his tribe scattered. Mangul
gone, Lin gone, Mankee gone, Marboo gone, Widjullee gone. Deven taken to the hills and Pooneem-
millar gone, Kummungeegut gone, Kerinbo gone, Kin
Aerry gone. And Tiger soon would be fleeing for *his*
life!

Nemarluk turned again towards the coast, walking
swiftly, his eyes fiercely roaming from side to side and
to the ground—always back towards the ground, to
Mother Earth who told him so much. But he saw no
more tracks, no broken bush, no trodden grass, no
bruised shrub or vine. Ears listening, his nostrils sought
every current of air, but he heard no sound of horses
or man, smelt no sweat of horse nor acrid tang of
smoke. He hurried on.

Where had these men come from? Where were their

horses? Where were their trackers? What was that one policeman doing all alone? Where was the rest of the patrol? A day's ride away? Or close by beside him?

Nemarluk now realized that he must outwit something far more dangerous than a tracker. He hurried on and lengthening shadows brought a rustling that was but of the wind. A bee-eater sped overhead with a flash of green and blue. There came the trill of its pretty song. How happy the bird was, and free!

Sunset brought a cold wind. Nemarluk shivered. By midnight he had covered fifty miles. He travelled quietly as a shadow fearful of what the night might hold. He kept to the shadows, though fearing them. He hurried across an open patch of country—to stand perfectly still, staring down. Dull starlight shone on a recently overturned stone.

Yes, and there were tracks—horses' tracks! He glared wildly around. But not a sound. He knew it now. The police were travelling fifty miles apart; a walking man, travelling east; a patrol, travelling east. They would cut the tracks of any man travelling north.

Nemarluk was travelling north! He stood there, glaring around. Where was this patrol camped? Or were they travelling all night, as he was? Where were their trackers? How many were there?

He remembered he had not disguised his tracks during this last fifty miles. They must find him. It did not matter what these tracks might tell him, all that mattered now was to speed far and fast. He started swiftly for the coast, his eyes wild as any hunted animal's, his ears set for the slightest sound, nostrils set for whiff of horse, or camp, for scent of white man or black. He had travelled seventy miles by dawn; but his powerful legs were set to leap forward and run if

necessary for miles. He sped noiselessly on into the
dawn, his killing spear gripped ready to strike, his
eyes seeking shadows that might not be shadows, his
heart in a burning rage.

Nemarluk, King of the Wilds, confused and hunted
in his own Wild Lands. A great longing surged within
him to hurry back to An-de-mallee camp, his own
home camp, to call his tribesmen around him. Almost
fearfully now he glanced around for he was travelling
alone in the night and around him were the spirits
of the night.

By midday next day he was near the coast and the
sea air smelt sweet in his nostrils. He sped on into a
maze of mangrove swamps, deep inlets of the sea,
sandhills and hollows dark-green under dense vine
jungle.

He pushed straight on another few miles and stepped
out of the scrub on to the shore. He threw up his head
and laughed at the sky, at the sea. He walked straight
on into the sea. Only then he stood, with water to his
knees. Ah! at last he could hide his tracks.

CHAPTER IX

THE PATROL CARRIES ON

NEMARLUK gazed along the tree-lined coast right and left. Neither man, woman, child nor dog was visible on beach, mud flat or sandbank. Only the herons, snipe, and plover and the lazy sea. The dense wall of trees behind him and the blue sky above.

Nemarluk turned north, walking through the shadows, watching out for fish and crabs. He was very tired, very hungry. But his mind was eased from that terrible dread of leaving his tracks behind him. Several miles farther on a shallow channel led directly inland. He turned along this channel, for it was a saltwater creek leading into the mangroves. There would be fish in it. Wading the water he entered the gloomy mangroves and fish scurried from his feet. His first spear chopped one in halves. He ate that fish raw, tearing it to pieces with his teeth. He speared three big fish, then saw the first crocodile lying up on a mudbank with its tail towards him, snipe and plover unconcernedly feeding around it. Another lay motionless on the opposite bank, yet another slaty shape farther on. But he waded on into the mangroves. Presently deep, dark waterholes would loom before him that he would not dare to wade.

When he came to these waterholes the snouts of big crocodiles were just visible above gloomy depths. Nemarluk left the creek and pushed his way deep into a dense vine jungle. It was as gloomy as moonlight, for countless saplings grew so close together that he had to walk sideways when passing through. Masses of

F

vines and creepers sent struggling tendrils up the trees, seeking sunlight far above. The ground was carpeted by a mass of leaves. Nemarluk pushed his way far in to where he felt sure no wandering crocodile could smell him. Then sat down and ate his fish raw, he would leave no tell-tale ashes of a fire. He lay on his side amongst the saplings and fell fast asleep.

He had lost his tracks in the sea and creek. Where he was now was impossible for horses to follow. Nor would his feet leave tracks that could be seen on this mass of leaves, in dense gloom. Even were it not so the bravest trackers would not dare to follow alone; that would surely mean death.

For hundreds of miles this part of the North Australian coast is deeply channelled by gloomy tidal creeks, swamps, river mouths, and salt arms of the sea. Muddy, dark-green, scummy, or deep and gloomy waterholes, full of crocodiles and hedged densely with vine scrub, are death traps to all but the truly experienced.

Nemarluk woke, staring into the blackness of the pit. He sat up, smelt decaying vegetation and a whiff from moving salt water. The mighty sea was heaving; soon the tide would be coming in. And then the night would be given over to creeping waters and to things that crawl and rage.

He sat deathly still as a cold body pressed upon his leg; he felt the slow tugging pressure as it pulled itself to his other leg and gripping, while still pressing and crawling lowered its head to the earth and pulled its long body across. Without a sound on the moist leaves the snake disappeared upon its business.

Nemarluk sat motionless, his staring eyes slowly tuning in to the darkness. This wild man's eyes began to glow slightly, to absorb night light so that he could sense things in darkness. Presently, he could partly

distinguish black rods, rods that were trunks of saplings. Eerie green glows of light glided past to vanish
then pulse into light again. Fire-flies these. And now
a glow of phosphorus upon decayed vegetation. His
ears were catching a faint hissing that is the breath
of night in primitive places such as this. Then came
an outraged bellow, a splash, then splash upon splash
as two bull crocodiles fought in some black hole in
the scrub.

A terrible loneliness came upon Nemarluk. He
wanted An-de-mallee his own home camp; he wanted
the camp fires and the corroboree songs; he wanted
his own Red Band; he wanted all his people; he
wanted Marboo.

He groped for his spears, stood up, stretched out his
arm and groped his way between the saplings. Leeches
sucked the blood from his legs, the bark of saplings
scraped his legs, his lips were parted, his eyes faintly
luminous as he followed his outstretched arm. He came
to a creek where the bank sloped suddenly into black
water. Cold air arose from scummy pools; fire-flies
glowed in space. Groping, he sought where the creek
would be narrowest. Tensely he stared down the blackness of muddy banks. Then, away down there, phosphorus streaked out. A glimpse of a black snout, the
lap of little water waves. Silence and darkness again.
He chose the narrowest part of the creek, guessed
where unseen black shapes might be lying in wait in
the mud, then leaped in and plunged for the invisible
bank.

He got there, and clawed straight up the mud to the
trees, leaping in among them in gasping relief.

But now a moan filled the air between the trees,
swept up every black creek, every tidal inlet. The tide
was rushing in filling the shallowest creeks deeply

and widely. The mouths of the creeks were in turmoil, for sharks came rushing in snapping amongst the swarm of fish and shark met crocodile to snap and run or snap and fight.

As Nemarluk stepped cautiously on a terrible uneasiness overtook him; he glanced behind again and again, listening. But no one could be following him; there was only the spirit world here, and the snakes, and the crocodiles, and the sharks. Those and the glowworms and fire-flies, the darkness and a million trees. He pressed on only to glare over his shoulder again and again. Someone was sending him a telepathic message; the harder he pressed on, the more insistent grew the message.

"Don't go! Don't go! Don't go!"

Nearly frantic now he pressed on, thinking of Marboo.

Soon, he was hemmed in. Deep, wide creeks were all around him. Impossible for him now to safely cross creek after creek. Soon it would be dawn. His arms found a tree at last with wide, spreading branches. He groped for a length of strong vine, and climbed up. Laid his spears carefully across the branches, settled himself comfortably, then lashed himself to the tree with the vine. Too well he knew the deep, drugged sleep that comes just before the dawn. At such a time an aboriginal may roll in the coals of a fire and burn terribly before he wakes. And Nemarluk did not want to fall from his tree in sleep. Crocodiles at high tide often crawl overland from creek to creek. And—their scent of meat is keen.

Nemarluk awoke in full sunlight. Birds were calling. Through the branches above sunlight filtered. Nemarluk glanced down, and snarled. Three big crocodiles lay waiting there, evenly apart, around the tree.

Nemarluk worked warmth into his limbs then undid the vine, and grasped his spears. He must not

waste a single spear. He did not fear these crocodiles, but he knew that one slip would mean death. He noted the clearest space between the trees behind two of the saurians, slipped to the ground and instantly ran straight towards a crocodile, only to leap straight towards the other, then immediately leap between them and away. He heard their twisting rush as they swerved around in pursuit, but he was away and dodging among the trees. He ran a little distance then steadied up and laughed.

Crocodiles can run with amazing speed a short distance on dry land, but are not so fast at turning and dodging.

Nemarluk carried on cheerfully all that day, his face laughing now as he pressed on to An-de-mallee camp. He hummed the war song of the Cahn-mah. Soon he would be with his friends.

He had covered many miles by late afternoon. Lengthening shadows brought a chill of loneliness. When the sun went down he looked suddenly behind. Again came that message. "Don't go! Don't go! Don't go!" Frowning, he pressed on, now travelling through forest country.

He slept like a dingo under an overhanging log. Awoke to a growing dawn. Stood cautiously erect. The first thing that caught his eye was the bent back of a kangaroo not a hundred yards away. He sighed his relief. The kangaroo would not be grazing so peacefully if danger threatened. Nemarluk fitted a spear to his wommera. He would kill the kangaroo, and eat again. For eternal vigilance is the law of the wild. The kangaroo had failed and must pay the penalty.

He cooked and ate portion of the 'roo; lit a smoke signal, and pressed on. He was supremely confident that long since he had completely outwitted any pursuers. The next day at sundown he was approaching An-de-mallee camp.

Presently, he heard the yelp of a dog, the laughter of a young lubra. He pressed eagerly on, then crouched low. Over the sand-dunes rose the wailing howl of a dingo. Then his call was answered. He leaped up and ran eagerly.

A loud, ringing cry greeted him. He raised his voice in reply and laughed to the skies. He ran on. Those that remained of his Red Band greeted him, and all the warriors, and the women and children all came running to meet him. Happily they crowded around him.

That night, the first for many nights, Nemarluk slept happily among the fires of his people. He missed Marboo.

It was daylight. Far away out near Talakinyin approaching a broken sandstone divide a line of pack-horses were picking their way down on to firmer country. Trackers riding ahead, then a policeman with the prisoners, and then another policeman in the rear. The two police had joined forces again. One of them, Ted Morey, had been walking at the rate of sometimes fifty miles a day, all on his own. While his mate, Jack Mahony, travelled with the horses by night to dodge the native look outs. Meeting again and again at rendezvous after rendezvous they had sometimes worked as far as fifty miles apart. Already, they had covered a thousand strenuous miles in the search for the elusive Nemarluk. Stern-faced men these, determined, resourceful. Beaten again and again, they came again and again. Doggedly they pushed on. Their horses were leg weary now, a tracker was gabbling with fever. But they would not turn back until horses and men were all done.

Marboo walked with them, her eyes terribly anxious. The patrol was travelling between Laberie and Paper-bark creeks. Over a divide the leading horses were disappearing as the prisoners climbed up behind them. Marboo suddenly stopped and lifted her foot with a pained expression, pulling at a thorn. Under lowered lids her black eyes were staring back at the big police-man, her heart beating wildly. The policeman dismounted to give his horse a chance and Marboo vanished amongst the rocks. A startled shout, a wheeling around of horses, but Marboo was leaping from rock to rock swift as a fleeing wallaby.

To An-de-mallee camp, one hundred and fifty miles away! Straight down on to the plains and on and on. On to Nemarluk.

Marboo travelled day and night, a wisp of the night, terrified of the spirits of the night. On to An-de-mallee! An-de-mallee and Nemarluk!

It was night at An-de-mallee camp. The tribesmen slept in huddled groups, their spears beside them. Not a leaf stirred, not a coal glowed. It seemed that night itself was sleeping the deep sleep of the wild man.

Suddenly a body flung itself upon Nemarluk. He

leaped up with out-thrust spear. . . . Marboo lay there panting, her eyes saying "Police!" She could not speak.

In hoarse gutturals Nemarluk woke the camp. Wild-eyed, they listened into the night.

The silence of the bush listened with them. A nankin bird glided by on silent wings.

Nemarluk took to the bush, and Marboo was beside him. A river barred their way. Nemarluk plunged in. Marboo swam beside him. There were crocodiles in that river.

Minmara fled downstream, Coon-an-pore and Me-al-cull with him.

The Red Band scattered to favourite hideouts. But others remained in camp. At dawn the dogs snarled. The camp listened and heard the dull thud of galloping hooves coming closer.

The tribesmen grinned at one another, then sat solemn-faced. Nemarluk and his Red Band would be scattered far and wide by now.

Nemarluk's band met again miles away, in the heart of a vine jungle near the beach. One by one they gathered cautiously to the rendezvous, silent as snakes gliding between the vines. Presently, there were twenty of them, all hard-bitten fighting men of the wilds.

They squatted there in the jungle, swapping experiences, laughing quietly. Ears keen, listening ever and anon, to lean toward one another and eagerly plan. They planned to cut off the trackers one by one.

Night came. Minmara crept out on to the open beach and there lit a small decoy fire. It twinkled bravely. Should police come out on to the beach a mile away they would see this fire. Would creep up and rush it, believing their quarry to be sleeping around it. The noise would wake the sleepers back in the jungle.

And noise did awaken the sleepers. Nemarluk and Minmara snatched their spears and were away almost over the tops of two startled trackers. Spear blades threatened rifle barrels, but the trackers ducked and the hunted men were past them slipping through the jungle like phantoms. Coon-an-pore, Nungpare, and Tunma fled together, the others scattered in all directions.

The hunted men sped on through jungle, then across salt arms and bog where it was impossible for horses to follow.

They came out on to forest country and made inland for the Moyle River, travelling through scrubs and the big messmate and woollybutt country, travelling faster than horses could travel. Night and day they travelled only easing up when in the Moyle.

The tribesmen in those savage lands greeted them with a rattling of spears and a furious challenge to the faraway police.

"Let us get together and kill them!" they yelled.

"Where is Tiger?" asked Nemarluk.

"Away in the Victoria."

"Chugulla?"

"With him."

"Tiger's men?"

"Scattered to the ranges until Tiger comes back."

"We can do nothing without Tiger's Mob," declared Nemarluk sullenly. "We will live with you until Tiger returns."

The tribesmen scowled. It was true. They could do nothing without a leader, they could only boast.

Nemarluk and Minmara needed rest after their long flight. But their rest by night was broken by dreams of a raid. By day they hid in the densest swamp, ears alert for the signal call that would tell them that danger drew near.

"These warriors are brave men when the police are not near," sneered Minmara. "Let them but hear the thud of galloping hooves and they will be away like the wind."

"Yes," agreed Nemarluk. "But they will warn us first if they can. They are good men, but they need Tiger's Mob to give them guts. Our own tribesmen are just the same as these—without the Red Band."

Minmara squatted silently, frowning into the gloom of the swamps. Half hidden by foliage some black and white geese were perched on the branch of a giant tree, yarning companionably. A male bird whistled softly. Receiving no answer from his larger spouse he tried to draw her into conversation with coaxing whistles. Still she spurned him. So the old-man goose arched his neck and broke out into a tirade of grunting cackles. The old lady refused to take this sitting down. Angrily she blew herself up, got a firmer grip of the branch with her yellow feet, puffed out her white breast and trumpeted angrily. Other of the male birds cackled and whistled softly, meekly enjoying the joke.

"The Red Band!" grunted Minmara savagely. "How we have been scattered—just because we have killed a few Jap men!"

"We will come together again," replied Nemarluk fiercely.

"Mangul, Lin, Mankee," said Minmara at last—"will they kill them?"

But Nemarluk frowned. He did not know what to answer. Full well he knew that the law of the wild is an eye for an eye, a tooth for a tooth, a life for a life.

And he believed the white man's law to be the same also.

A week later they were camped with the tribesmen at Narvee camp, in jungle by the Moyle River. A sleeper in the night awoke and heard the call of a dingo.

He listened. Presently, the dingo called again, and at the very end of the long drawn howl the listener detected the very faintest sign of a cough. He threw back his head and answered. At the end of his call a practised ear would detect the faintest sign of a holding of breath, as if the dingo had almost coughed just at the very last. Then away in the distance rose a mournful howl. The listener sprang up and awoke the others.

They grouped together, clenching their spears, staring into the night. The dingo did not call again. Just before daylight they were shadows flitting through the jungle.

The police crept into their camp to find the coals still warm.

"And we did not make a sound," frowned Morey.

"I believe the night birds whisper them we are coming," shrugged Mahony. "We'll have the job to do all over again."

"Anyway we won't have to light a fire," answered Morey brightly. "Get the boys to put the quart pots on while I knock up a few johnny-cakes for breakfast."

All that day from the swamps of the great Did-ee plain swarms of ducks arose that at times seemed to darken the sky. Ducks that told of the presence both of the hunters and the hunted. For the tribesmen though avoiding the police were not afraid of them; it was Nemarluk and Minmara the police were after.

So they hunted as they travelled, ever wading farther

into the swamps, and in laughing shouts to one another joking at the terrible fix the patrol would find themselves in as they were drawn farther and farther into the morass. Now and then, in the tangled bush dividing swamp from swamp they would get a glimpse of Table Top Mountain standing like a majestic sentinel far out in the centre of the plain.

Late afternoon came, bringing its long shadows. Then, the afterglow of the sun. Evening fell. The police patrol had travelled twenty-eight miles through bog and swamp, a terrible trip for horses, mules and men. Wearily they camped. And phantom tribesmen stampeded their horses in the night.

CHAPTER X

THE RAID

POLICE and trackers spent an anxious day in guarding camp while rounding up their horses. By that time the tribesmen were thirty miles away. They left plain tracks for the police to follow.

But Nemarluk and Marragin cunningly doubled back towards the coast. A few days later and they were back at An-de-mallee camp. Here Nemarluk collected his scattered tribe, then led them into the sandhill country between Nan-yar Plain and the coast. Secure in hideouts there they led a nomadic life. . . . Until one late afternoon a smoke signal warned them: "Police!" They fled, just in time.

For week after week, Nemarluk was closely hunted now; allowed no rest; a patrol was ever at his heels. With the remainder of his Red Band sullenly marching beside him he led his tribe across the plains into the swamps, out again to forage the forest lands. When harried from here he doubled back to the coast and the morasses by the sea. He hid on the beach flanked by salt-water creeks and with a wall of mangroves behind him; he hid in the vine jungles among the sand-dunes.

One night Nemarluk was almost surrounded there. He and his horde, crawling on their bellies, escaped through the ring and gained the open forest. He travelled his people eighty miles a day to the Wangan Ranges, then away to the jungles around the Moyle. Exhausted at times they would just flop down where

night caught them. Hunt for food the next day, then
begin the unending flight again.

Nemarluk was mad with rage. Not only was he
being hunted ceaselessly, but the life of the tribe was
broken; they were hunted and hungry and bewildered.
There was plenty of fish now in the sea and creeks,
but they were hunted from the creeks. There was food
in the swamps—they were hunted from the swamps.
There was food in the sand-dunes—they were hunted
from the dunes. There was bird life on the plains,
plentiful yams, too. They were hunted from the plains.
Constantly now they were kept on the alert and the
march, ever marching over foodless country, seldom
resting more than a day in country where food was
plentiful. Striding along at the head of his tribe,
Nemarluk raged against the white police, who
instinctively seemed to know just where he would
make for next; knew just where the yams grew best;
knew where the plum-trees were in fruit, where the
wild geese were nesting; knew where fishing was best,
where the best waterholes were, where the ducks and
swans and water-hens were plentiful.

Nemarluk grew madder as the weeks dragged by.
This ceaseless flight meant the tribe had no time to
prepare for the ceremonies of the making of the young
men, for the ceremonies to the seasons and the hunt;
no time at all for their important ceremonial life; no
time for anything but snatch a little sleep, hurriedly
hunt game, then march, march, march. By night and
by day the warriors, the women and young people,
even the piccaninnies, would start at the slightest
sound, the thud of a wallaby in the grass, the uneasy
call of a bird, the moaning of the wind, the creak of a
tree branch, the call of a dingo, the hoot of an owl.
They would stare at every broken stick seeking the

story it might tell; peer at every wind-blown tuft of grass; watch every flight of a bird and stare around and listen—listen.

Of his Red Band, only Minmara and Marragin remained now. Striding fast at the head of his tribe the others now followed exactly in his footsteps and those of Minmara and Marragin, thus blotting them out, stamping out the tell-tale footprints.

But yet again smoke signals arose, danger signals. Nemarluk headed straight for the mountains.

"We will lure them deep into the Valley of the Dead," he growled to Minmara. "Their horses cannot travel there. When we get them tired and hungry we will spear them from the rocks one by one. We can wait no longer for Tiger's Mob."

"Why has he not come sooner?" complained Nung-pare.

"He is busy on the Victoria," frowned Nemarluk. "There may be police there, too. We do not know what is happening away across there."

"The day will dawn when I will bury my spear in the heart of tracker Splinter," growled Minmara ferociously.

"I shall cut Bogey's liver out," said Marragin simply.

"I will kill Bul-Bul," declared Nemarluk, "and then we will fall upon the white police."

"Cut them to pieces just as Tiger's Mob did the white men," hissed Minmara. "What a day it will be!"

"There are enough of us to attack them," growled Coon-an-pore. "And we are savage!"

As they drew near the mountains a smoke arose from a sandstone bluff.

"They are on our tracks," laughed Nemarluk.

"They are never off them," sneered Me-al-cull. "They

must guess you are still with the horde because we keep travelling, travelling, travelling."

"We will soon use our spears," hissed Minmara. "Let us hurry the women on; the children are lagging behind."

"Yes," agreed Marragin, "hurry on and prepare the trap. Don't walk on our tracks now," he shouted to the men behind. "Let them see the tracks of Nemarluk. We will lure them on."

But from the look out rose a puff of black smoke followed by another then another, and then a ring of smoke with a black puff shooting straight up through it. Slowly the smoke drifted away.

They halted, staring at one another. This was an urgent danger signal.

"It may be Bul-bul," said Nemarluk doubtfully. "He may lie in wait in the ranges. We have not yet seen his tracks with the police who follow out tracks. We are not sure where he is."

Silently they waited.

"There is danger ahead," growled Minmara at last, "and danger behind us."

Suddenly, Nemarluk felt the call of his own home country of An-de-mallee camp. When imminent danger threatened he always felt that call. With a grunt he pressed on, turning parallel with the foothills. They followed.

Nemarluk lost their tracks in a lily lagoon, made a wide detour and camped on a muddy island, the piccaninnies shivering at the chattering of the bats. At dawn they commenced wading to dry land. Nan-nar-ree was bitten on the leg by a yellow-bellied water-snake. She screamed and shook the thing off and hurried after them, fear in her eyes. Any who get sick or hurt are left behind in a flight such as this. It is the law of the wild. Nemarluk led them back straight to the coast.

A fortnight passed, and they had rest. It was the season when the white gum flowers fill the air with their sweetish lemon smell. Myriads of shrieking flying foxes were dining upon the flowers. The tribe ate ravenously, causing havoc in the flying-fox colonies. There was abundance of fish, too, in among the mangrove roots all along the banks of the salt-water creeks. Eagerly they speared the fish while the women gathered dilly-bags full of shell-fish, eel, and crab. With bellies full again they relaxed by the cooking fires deep in a jungle scrub. They had shaken off the police. They joked now at the dance they had led them; a lad earned great laughter by mimicking the police struggling with a bogged horse.

It was the flying foxes that put them away. A dense mass of foxes chattering, shrieking upon and above the trees as the hunters hurled throwing sticks up amongst them. Those screeches, that black cloud of agitated flying foxes could be heard and seen for miles.

And the trackers saw them. Sundown came, then that misty haze which is almost like violet air dying into evening. The huntsmen in two and fours came singing into Il-lin-ee camp. The women were straggling in, each laden with her day's catch. The cooking fires were lit, laughter broke out, the warriors threw their game by the fire to squat and gossip over the day's chase, awaiting the cooking of the meal.

Nemarluk, the cunning, with Minmara, never entered a camp now until after dark. He remembered what had happened far away on the Victoria River. But Marragin, returning in the lead with a band of late warriors laughed at his warnings; for Marragin and his men that day had had good hunting. They were hungry, too, and now smelt the smoke of the cooking fires from the hidden camp.

"The police are far away," declared Marragin. "May the dingoes be gnawing their bones." With a song upon his lips he led the way into camp.

Men rose from his very feet, the spears were snatched from his hand.

Marragin snarled then hooted warningly, his last service to Nemarluk.

That night, Nemarluk with Minmara crept towards the outskirts of the camp. On a big white tree Nemarluk silently carved a picture of the *Ouida,* carved it deep into the bark with a knife he had fashioned from the ironwork of the vessel. In the morning, the big white policeman saw the carving.

"Look at this!" he called admiringly to his mate. "Nemarluk's visiting card! He's as game as they make them."

They stared at the picture on the tree.

"It's the *Ouida* all right," declared Mahony. "I'd recognize it anywhere. Just a few crude lines cut in the bark, but it's the *Ouida.*"

"He's doubled back to An-de-mallee camp if I know my man," declared Morey. "Quick! Saddle up and we'll be there by sundown!"

That night, Nemarluk and a remnant of his people were camped deep within a dense vine jungle. Around this camp but two hundred yards from them glowed little, dull fires. Decoy fires.

At dawn, from all sides, men rushed past the decoys and dashed farther into the jungle. Dogs yelped, a lubra screamed, warriors snatched spears. Nemarluk and Minmara were already running and again they ran straight on top of two trackers who ducked from the upraised spears. Nemarluk was away again.

They fled to the mangroves, the crocodiles, the bogs and salt arms of the sea. Savage now they lived in the dense jungle that hedges the gloomy water-holes where the crocodiles lurk. Their food was fish and they wolfed it raw. They took the fish from under the very snouts of the saurians, and defied them. Day by day, night by night, they waited for the police and trackers.

"When they come they will come like snakes crawling through the jungle," hissed Minmara; "each man will be wide apart from his mate. We will spring on them and kill them one by one, slowly strangle them, man after man, and not make a sound. Then!" he snarled, and his eyes flashed, "we will feed their bodies to the crocodiles!"

But the police did not come.

"We won't go in there after them," decided the taller policeman. "We would never find them in that morass; the trackers would be too scared to attempt it anyway. We'll ride a hundred miles south as if searching for tracks, then say we believe they've fled to the ranges. As soon as they know we've gone, they'll come out."

And a week later Nemarluk and Minmara "came out".

"They have gone," declared Minmara.

"Yes," scowled Nemarluk, "and when we least expect them they will be upon us again."

"Call your men together," advised Minmara. "Kill them!"

"How can I?" snarled Nemarluk. "Of the Red Band, only we two are left. Tiger's Mob are back on the Victoria River, Deven's men hide in the ranges away across the Victoria. My best warriors are scattered far and wide into the groups. The others are only hunters, not warriors. And they have been chased night and day throughout three moons; have seen the Red Band caught and are frightened."

"Let us kill the police ourselves!" frowned Minmara.

"Kill two white police and three times our number of trackers?" answered Nemarluk. "Easy, if they were fools. We know they are not fools."

Minmara looked from under lowering brows.

"Are we to be hunted for ever like dingoes?" he snarled.

"There is not only the one patrol to kill," growled Nemarluk. "There must be another threatening the people on the Fitzmaurice. We do not know where it is. I want to fight as much as you do, but we would be fools to fight without Tiger's Mob and Deven's men. We will join up sooner or later; *then* we will fight and give their bones to the hawks and dingoes. Now, let us save ourselves that we may live to fight."

They lit a signal fire to call the scattered people together. From the forest, the jungle, the mangroves, the plains and the sandhills day by day the family groups straggled in, wild-eyed, fearful. Each arrival was greeted with glad cries; they ran together, children shrieking to children. Truly, they looked like hunted men and women now joyfully gaining confidence in the regathering of the horde. Presently nearly all the horde were assembled again. There was great gossip around the fires at night; laughter now in the chase; busy work at mending spears and weapons. The tools and weapons of aboriginals need constant repair under hard work, just as our tools and weapons do. The dilly-bags of the women were becoming threadbare, many a coolamon had been lost in flight, burnt accidentally, or broken in use. Every one was busy while keeping a sharp look out.

By this time the patrol was again on their tracks. The man hunt went on, for the white law is inexorable. Nemarluk and Minmara had killed Japanese men. They must answer to the law.

Nemarluk hurried his people away almost to the tall, rocky barriers of Hermit Hill, then on almost to the headwaters of the Daly. A shrewd move that, for lower down river was the Daly River Police Station. But the policeman there was wideawake, so Nemarluk doubled back and made for the Wangan Range. Among these rocky bluffs, heavily wooded with wolly-butt and paper-bark, the horde gained sanctuary for a time. Gratefully they trekked deeper in among the ranges to Wangan Waterfalls. Amid this wild beauty waterfowl were plentiful, kangaroo and wallaby grazed on grassy swards near the singing falls.

Up among the rocks the wild plum-trees were in fruit. Eagerly women and children gathered dilly-bags full of fruit, then squatting down hammered them between stones into squashed masses that they rounded by hand into lumps like cricket balls. These they set on the hot rocks to sunbake. When set hard they could carry them till needed for food.

The men hunted with the silent earnestness of desperately hungry men. A fortnight of this good feeding, of almost restful nights, and they began to feel men again.

But one dark night a dog suddenly howled—and the horde were away. Nemarluk hurried them past the foothills; and some days later they were crossing Did-ee Plain and on to Jan-Jar-roo, sentinal of the plains. To give the sore-footed ones a chance they stayed here hunting the plains until their look out on Jan-jar-roo spied a far-distant patrol.

Nemarluk led them inland making for the ranges

that head the Fitzmaurice, but when nearly there a swiftly travelling patrol blocked them from joining up with Chugulla's men. Nemarluk doubled back and away across the plains again to the coast. By now a few of the women and children were straggling, their feet cracked and sore. But they clung to the horde and Nemarluk clung to them. Gratefully they came to rest at In-dar-roo camp. Here, they were raided again. In the dead of night they faced a cold wind as they flitted through the sandhill country and out again on to the plains, hurrying back to the Moyle.

Fierce men were on the tracks of the hunters. The hunters were hunted. Night came.

The patrol camped at Bar-ram-lone waterhole set in its tangled scrub. The big policeman and two trackers quietly rode away. No eyes should see them. They would be fifty miles away at dawn, seeking Nemarluk where he least expected them.

The hunters crouched in a vine thicket, the circlets of white ochre around their eyes, the bars of white across their greased bodies denoting men who had sworn to kill. They gripped their deadly spears as a scout glided amongst them and hissed:

"The big policeman and two trackers have ridden away!"

Nemarluk threw back his head; he wanted to roar with laughter. But only his eyes were dancing. He bent towards his warriors and hissed:

"We have them! There is only one policeman left, and four trackers. Before the dawn we will cut them to pieces. And then—we will hunt the other one!"

Minmara bent low. He was sharpening to razor-edge his spears by softly rubbing one blade against another. Their hands were clenching and unclenching; a war-

rior's teeth gritted between hissing breath. Vengeance
was very near.

Night drew on toward the old dawn hour. Phantom
forms were crawling close around the sleeping camp,
phantoms with blazing eyes.

Tracker Charlie crouched with his back to a tree
staring into the night, his every sense alert. By this very
tree twelve moons ago he was speared on a night such
as this. Vividly he recalled that sharp spear biting into
his leg, the scream as he leaped away from the yelling
figures stabbing at him from the dark. Only the quick
guns of the police had saved him. And now here he
was again. And tracking—Nemarluk.

It was Charlie who, beside this very tree had been
on watch the night Mooderish attacked Constables
Hoffman and Hemming's patrol. So to-night, of
course, he could not sleep. Which was why the cunning policeman had given him the dangerous night
watch. Fearfully he stared; listened; smelt out into the
night.

All was a deathly silence with not even a faint current of air that might bring him the scent of greased
bodies crawling, crawling towards him.

They saw Charlie, the dark blot of his peering head
betrayed him. They crawled very close, they waited for
two breathless hours. But Charlie showed not the
slightest sign of dozing, Charlie was a very frightened,
very alert man.

Then Charlie heard the hoot of an owl. It really
was an owl, but it was enough for the nerves of Charlie.
Frantically he was awakening the sleepers.

"Quick! Quick!" he hissed. "Wild men all around
about! They come! They come!"

Instantly policemen jumped out into the dark and knelt with rifles ready.

Nemarluk was furious. But his men held steady, not a sound. Then came the faintest breeze—and the trackers smelt the oiled bodies.

Each man peered along the barrel of his rifle knowing that if the rush came he was a dead man.

Nemarluk's men waited until dawn, but the patrol never relaxed vigilance for an instant. Both Nemarluk and Minmara were burning to charge, but they knew they would charge alone. The warriors would charge a sleeping camp, but not wideawake men with rifles. The long-continued chase had daunted their nerves.

With the coming of dawn they melted away.

The chase continued. But the police horses were now leg weary, the food too had almost given out. The patrol was encumbered with prisoners, witnesses and sick people. At last they could go no farther. They had travelled fourteen hundred miles in three months, often over terribly rough country. Reluctantly the patrol turned the weary horses' heads back towards the Daly River. The patrol left the Wild Lands.

And the primitives were rejoiced in many a wild camp. Nemarluk and Minmara were heroes who had beaten the while police.

Time passed.

Nemarluk and Minmara with their tribesmen were hunting. From a far-spread, sun-cracked swamp they had burned the dried reeds and rushes; thick black smoke had formed a rolling black cloud above them all day. To-morrow they would find where many turtles lay hidden. For when the swamps dry up the land, turtle burrow deep down while mud is still there. The sun dries the mud almost hard as rock.

But the turtle are deep below, following the last of the water down, awaiting the distant day when the big rains shall come again.

The tribesmen, camping in a pandanus palm thicket talked of the turtle they would find in the morning. For the sunbaked mud, no matter how cracked and crinkled it might be, would bear clear traces of where the turtle had burrowed down several months ago. Minmara crooned a hunting song and all joined in. As the moon waned they cuddled around their fires to sleep.

Dawn came. Minmara awoke with strong hands upon him; he glared up into the grinning face of Bul-bul.

Startled grunts; thud of bodies flung violently aside. Then a crashing in the thicket told of Nemarluk's escape.

CHAPTER XI

A TRAP IS SET FOR NEMARLUK

NEMARLUK now roamed alone. He made towards the Victoria River, determined to join Tiger if he was in from the bush, Deven otherwise. The big chief was a vengeful man. His Red Band was now slowly travelling hundreds of miles away towards the white man town of Darwin. His Red Band, the pride of the wilds, every man a captive!

Nemarluk's fierce eyes glared up to the skies, glared out over the plain and towards the blue of the McAdam Range. A flock of cockatoos flew noisily overhead, free as the wind. But to the wild man there was a moaning in the air for a breeze was blowing among the casuarinas and their long, thin leaves were swishing, sobbing.

Gritting his teeth Nemarluk shook his spears and sped on into a strong wind. He followed a buffalo pad until it led deep into the brown desolation of a dried-up marsh now a sea of dead rushes and weeds. From a nutmeg-tree he broke two light, dry sticks. He fluffed a handful of dry grass and sharply sawed the sticks upon it. The grass smouldered, a spark shot up, the grass burst into flame. Nemarluk threw kindling upon it and the fire leaped up. From a paper-bark tree he tore a long strip of bark, dangled the end in the flame. The oily bark caught alight. Nemarluk walked along, trailing the blazing bark. The dry grass behind him caught alight.

Within twenty minutes clouds of black smoke, crimson with flame, were rolling towards the sky. The wind blew the flames which leaped and sped over mile upon mile of country. The crackling of a huge grass fire roared behind him.

Thus, lighting strip after strip of bark and trailing it behind him, Nemarluk set the country alight. And that fire, raging along behind him blotted out his tracks as he walked along. Now swiftly following him swarmed clouds of brown kites crying "Eek-eek-eek-eek" as they planed into the smoke, wolfing grasshoppers and rats fleeing for their lives. Night came and the darkness behind Nemarluk was a raging mass of flame. Let them track him now who could. It was impossible.

That night the scorched earth was beautiful but terrifying.

Nemarluk walked on, edging towards the coast as the hours went by. It was almost light as day. He had plenty of company; the light, the roar of the fire, the flurried flight of startled birds, the "thud! thud! thud!" of escaping wallaby or 'roo. If the wind changed Nemarluk would be forced to escape himself. But he knew how.

By midnight the wind began to die down. Soon, he must take to the water to lose his tracks for the wind no longer would spread new flames along.

He took to the water sooner than he expected. Glanced behind into furious, red-rimmed little eyes within a massive skull from which two great horns

were charging upon him. Nemarluk leaped ahead with
the bull buffalo at his heels.

That smoke-blinded buffalo gave Nemarluk the run
of his life straight across open country, man and beast
racing for life in the glare of the flames. There was
not a tree to climb, Nemarluk raced straight for a
salt-water bog with thunder of beast and flames at
his heels. Reaching the bog with only a few yards to
spare, he leaped straight out upon it where the buffalo,
with a furious grunt, sank nearly to its chest.

Nemarluk stood panting, snarling at the raging beast
struggling its way back out of the bog. It plunged
back out of the mud to turn and stand shaking its
neck and horns. Nemarluk rattled his spears towards
it but dared not hurl a spear lest he lose the precious
weapon.

Growling to himself at the fright the buffalo had
given him he picked his way across the bog to where
it ran into a long arm of the sea, a shallow creek deep
inland in the mangroves. He took to the water walking with the receding tide. The sea was miles away
but time did not matter now; his pursuers would long
since have been turned back by the fire. For thirty
miles to-day the fire had covered his tracks; for thirty
miles to-morrow the sea would cover his tracks. Who
then, could find Nemarluk?

He strode cautiously on with spear arm held ready
as his fierce eyes glared to right and left for prowling
crocodiles; and found a big one. It lay straight across
the shallow, rapidly emptying creek; Nemarluk saw its
serrated back just above the water. Only the eyes of a
tensely alert wild man could have distinguished that
black log lying there almost submerged in the falling
tide.

Nemarluk halted. The crocodile waited. If Nemarluk climbed the bank and walked around the brute, it would mean that here at least he must leave tracks. To throw a spear meant that he might lose a precious weapon, for the crocodile would crush the haft to splinters. Nemarluk gazed around, then warily waded back to a heap of driftwood. He pulled out the heaviest sticks and broke them into three-foot lengths, then carried them back, measured the distance, aimed at the horny ridge around the crocodile's eyes, and threw. The first stick broke square across the crocodile's skull. Its ugly snout jerked up and it slewed downstream with a startled grunt. Nemarluk threw rapidly to hasten its going, putting his practised weight into every throw. Then cautiously followed on. The creek bottom was of white sand, the water clear and very shallow; there was still the glow of the fire in the sky. It was starlight too and the moon was rising. Nemarluk carefully watched the mangrove edge and dark creek banks. Again and again the crocodile waited for him; again and again he drove it on. The big saurian knew well that this was only one man, one man alone in the night.

After a mile of this slow wading Nemarluk grew a little careless; became used to the black log waiting for him every two or three hundred yards downstream. He determined to give it something to remember him by next time. Yes, there it was again, waiting right across the stream, just where a shaft of moonlight fell clearly among the mangroves. Nemarluk edged closer gripping tight his heaviest stick. He would rattle the fangs of the thing with the next blow; it would move then and keep on moving. He crept closer, angry at this cunning thing that was delaying him so. He flung back his arm—then leaped for the bank as it charged with amazing speed, seeming to leap across the water with its great tail urging it on. With flying leaps Nemarluk reached the bank tingling to a vicious grunt and clash of jaws at his heels. He ran on through the mangroves; only the tangle of the roots saved him. He sped on to open land glorious under moonlight then hurried on towards the sea, very much shaken.

Nemarluk hurried on over the sand and vines, peering at every dark patch of scrub. His teeth gritted furiously. Chased by the white police; chased by the trackers; chased by the animals; chased by the crocodiles—everything was against him. In a fury of anger and loneliness he strode cautiously on.

Next day he was wading the sea edge, walking south along the beach with the water washing out his tracks. The seagulls kept him company, the snipe and plover on the mudbanks, long legged oyster-eaters ran before him in the shallows. Now and again he speared a fish, if it was small and tasty he tore it to pieces with his teeth and ate it as he walked. If it was big he hung it to his belt, the belt that Marboo had made. The sky was nearly white, the sun gleamed down on lazy waves and green of mangrove, casuarina, and scrub.

By midday Nemarluk was very tired, very hungry, very lonely. He came ashore up along a creek mouth, crawled into a vine jungle and hid himself. There he ate, then coiled himself up and fell asleep.

During the next ten days Nemarluk wandered along that maze of the coast right to the wide mouth of the Fitzmaurice. Eagerly here along the bays and tidal inlets he sought the sheltered camping places of Chugulla's people; those coastal camps to which they wandered in fishing seasons when the coastal lands grew ripe fruits and seashore yams. But every camp

was wind beaten and abandoned, only the bones of
last season lay there, burnt sticks and turtle shell half
buried in sand. There was neither people, nor charcoal,
nor track of man or dog. Nemarluk was disappointed,
although he knew they would be far away up towards
the head of the river, ready for escape into the ranges
should danger threaten. Amongst this wild expanse
of timber-girt waters he felt very lonely, his mates the
wild birds, the sky, and the crocodiles. He wished
Marragin was with him; he longed for Minmara, for
Mangul, for Lin, and Mankee—for any of his Red
Band. He wished Marboo was here.

He swam the river on a log and pushed on through
the wild tangle towards the far flung mouth of the
Victoria. He stared out at the islands and miles of
water pouring into Queen's Channel. There was no
smoke, no sign of life there either. He turned down
along the river mouth walking inland to Blunder Bay.
But the islands there showed no sign of life, nor did
the river shore. He had expected fresh track of people
long before this. The people must be all up river. He
hurried up along beside the broad river until he came
to a signal place. Here he lit a smoke, and waited.
The answer came in late afternoon far away across
river—from Deven's look out.

All was clear on both sides of the river.

Nemarluk snatched his spears with an eager smile
and hurried along the river bank. That night at his
favourite spot he launched a log and swam across.
Noiselessly he hurried on through the bush to the
native camp. Cautiously he approached though eager
to meet friends, to talk and to eat and to smell the
camp fires of people. He listened for a snatch of
corroboree song, for the clicking of kylies, the bark
of a dog. Warily he drew closer and soon was circling

the camp, listening to the voices, the snatches of corroboree song, the shrill laughter following some
woman's joke.

He recognized many of those voices; smiled at the
sound of some, frowned at others. He crept closer
until, by the fires, he could see the black shapes of
men's bodies squatting there yarning, crooning, making spears, or lazily gossiping. A piccaninny here and
there was chewing a bone, watched by an expectant
dog. Nemarluk lifted up his head and the howl of a
dingo floated to the skies.

Presently there came the "Wow-wow! Wow-wow!"
of a boobook owl. Nemarluk leaped forward and strode
into the camp, smiling in boyish delight. They stared
towards him, the kylie sticks ceased clicking, tousle-
haired women looked up with brightening eyes, old
warriors grinned, welcoming cries broke out. With a
wave of the hand Nemarluk smiled at them all and
strode straight to Deven's fire.

"Wah!" he smiled.

"Wah!" grinned Deven, and "Wah! Wah! Wah!"
echoed the fierce men around him.

Nemarluk dropped his spears and squatted down,
they gave him the warmest place on the sand right
over the fire. He gorged on the food they brought him;
a hunk of roast wallaby with a length of snake and
a handful of yams. How good this food tasted, roasted
on the cooking fires of the people! Washed down by
strong tea—white man's tea. How Nemarluk gulped
that tea! The people crowded around him, pressed
him to eat and smoke. That was his crowning delight,
to smoke. It was Deven's pipe. A bashful station boy
offered a stick of tobacco. Nemarluk broke it with
his thumbs, stuffed the pipe, leaned to the fire and

H

picked up a live coal with his fingers. He puffed and
puffed.

"Wah!" he smiled. "It's good!"

"Tobacco," grinned Deven, "tobacco and iron. If the
white men had not these two things our people would
never work for them. These two things chain our
people to the whites. Curse them."

All grouped around Deven's fire, warriors and renegades and station boys; bush blacks and tame blacks,
women and children wide-eyed listening far into the
night to Nemarluk's stories of his outwitting of the
white police. Deven listened carefully, his gleaming
eyes watching the rapt expression on the faces of those
around. A strong warrier, this Deven; strong of char-
acter too, his cruel, defiant mouth tight shut as he
listened and gauged the feeling of those around.

It was near daylight when Nemarluk and Deven
picked up their spears and vanished.

"We've got them tamed," muttered Deven. "But he
sleeps soundly who does not sleep in a camp."

"Yu ai!" agreed Nemarluk grimly. "The dingo hiding in a hollow log is safer than the hunted one who
sleeps amongst his people. But your warriors? What
men have you got around you now?"

"Good men. I picked them, they were eager to take
the place of Kerinbo and Kinterry, Kummungeegut
and Booneemillar and the others. These are nearly as
good, though I wish I had my own men back."

"They are far away now," said Nemarluk sadly, "in
that white man's jail with my Red Band. I wish they
could escape. Do you think they will kill them?"

"The ways of the white men are strange," frowned
Deven. "throughout many moons our men again and
again have been taken to that Darwin jail. Some have
never returned; their spirits alone have come back to

whisper by the river. Others whom we made sure the white men would kill they allowed to come back to us."

Nemarluk frowned. "If ever they catch me, I don't think I'll come back."

"You won't. They want you for the killing of the Jap men. That is against their law. And they kill a man who kills against their law."

"So do we," agreed Nemarluk cheerfully, "—when we catch him!"

"They haven't caught you yet," laughed Deven.

"They never will!" declared Nemarluk fiercely.

Deven frowned in the darkness, striding rapidly on. He remembered that long ago he had used those words in that very tone of voice. And—*they* had got *him!*

Next day, high up on Deven's eyrie they discussed their plans.

"There is only one white policeman now in my country," said Deven. "He is away up river at Timber Creek. Bul-bul and Splinter the trackers are with him, the other trackers do not matter much. He is shoeing his horses, mending harness, packing food in cases, making all ready for a big patrol. He will come seeking you again; his black spies sit quietly in every camp; he has one, too, on every station, riding with the stockboys. But—we know what he does, we know his every move. We will know when he comes seeking you and we'll know whether he comes down this side of the river, or strikes away out towards the Fitz-maurice and Chugulla's country?

"Tiger?" inquired Nemarluk eagerly.

"At Bradshaw station," grinned Deven, "working in white man's clothes. Tiger is a good worker, works hard and does what they tell him—when he wants to. Tiger does not skulk away back in the ranges boasting of what he has done and what he will do when they come after him. Tiger is the most daring of our men and very clever. Right under their noses he watches what they do. He knows their every move. His mob are back on the Fitzmaurice."

"Then they don't know yet that Tiger's Mob killed the white men?"

"No. And every one along the river has kept a quiet tongue. Tiger will know as soon as the police know; Tiger trusts no one. Tiger will make his plans as soon as he knows that the police know. He will act far ahead of them, before they even guess he knows they are after him."

"How long will it be before some snake in the grass gives tongue?"

"No man can tell that!" frowned Deven. "No whisperer has yet been game to chance losing his tongue —and his kidney fat. But Tiger has enemies. . . . They will find a way sooner or later."

"And Tiger works there right under the policeman's nose," smiled Nemarluk. "No wonder I could not find him."

"Of course not," laughed Deven. "Neither will the policeman find him—when he wants him! But it is a great joke. The policeman has told Bul-bul to find out what has happened to those two white men who canoed away seeking the yellow stone. They have been gone many moons now; they canoed away down river —and vanished. Bul-bul is to find out why they are so long away. And why no one has heard of them."

"I'd like to cut Bul-bul's tongue out," said Nemarluk pleasantly, "but I'd rather take his kidney fat."

"You'll get it some day," promised Deven, "if Tiger doesn't do the job for you."

Nemarluk threw out clenched fists. "I want my men!" he said fiercely. "I want men around me. All my Red Band have gone. I want Tiger and Tiger's Mob; I want you and your men. I want to fight the police, to drive the white men out of our country."

"I have a plan!" grinned Deven.

Nemarluk stared eagerly.

"The white police will come down this side of the river to make sure you are not here. They must do so. If you are here they must catch you or drive you back to your own country. When they come, you cross. Leave your tracks plain on the other side and make back towards your own country, taking your time. The white police must ride back up the river to cross their horses; they must travel a hundred miles up, and more when they turn to ride down along the opposite side, for they must ride away out bush to cut the Baines and Buller rivers. When they arrive back opposite they will cut your tracks. And when they are in full chase we will signal you. Then we will dog *their* tracks; Tiger's Mob, and all the good men I know down river, and any of your own men you can signal to cut across country and meet us. Together we will dog the tracks of the police while you turn inland and gradually decoy them into the Fitzmaurice country, then on up the river head, and on into the ranges. We will be on their tracks, half a day's march behind them. When we get them all in a narrow place, some deep gorge of Tiger's choosing, we will fall upon them. One night, just as they are creeping out to fall upon you."

Nemarluk laughed loud and long. Some of the boyishness had come back to his face.

"It is a good plan," he agreed eagerly. "I hope the police come soon; my spear itches to bury itself in Bul-bul."

"We'll get him sometime," said Deven confidently, and stood up. Nemarluk stood beside him, they gazed away out and down over plain and river.

Near, hidden by trees, was the roof of a pioneer homestead, the nearest neighbour was forty miles away; none for nearly three hundred miles across river. Cattle, like toy goats, were browsing away down there; a little brown patch was a mob of horses. Down there at the native camp a wisp of smoke slowly rose as some woman started a fire. From a patch of scrub a horse and rider sauntered, then another and another. All the rest was the ramparts of the rand, the plain, the winding river, the sunlight and the sky.

"How about a wallaby hunt?" suggested Deven.

"Yu ai," agreed Nemarluk.

They turned and with lithe, effortless steps picked their way down the crag, leaping from rock to rock down into a deep gorge and on into the ranges. Two perfect specimens of alert primitive men at home in this wild setting.

Away up river at the tiny Timber Creek outpost Constable Fitzer was thinking deeply. Nemarluk had proved himself one of the cleverest and most determined aboriginals ever to fall foul of the law. To catch him by ordinary patrol means was impossible. It would need a much deeper scheme than that. And the scheme came to Fitzer.

The *Maroubra* was due. The *Maroubra* is a small sea-going launch that every three or four months brings supplies from Darwin to the lonely river stations. Fitzer grinned to himself, thinking deeply as he kept busily on with preparations for his patrol. Mustering the horses and mules, picking out the twenty fittest, strongest animals. Overhauling the gear and packsaddles, packing the spare horseshoes, the neck chains, the bells, locks, handcuffs, horseshoe nails, shoeing kit, hobbles. Packing the foodstuffs and equipment, the swags, tomahawk, tent, camp-sheet, camp-oven, billycans, pannikins, quart pots, knives, ammunition; the bags of flour, cases of jam, the bullybeef and dried salt beef, soda, cream of tartar, salt, pepper, tinned butter, etc. All the necessary things needed on a long patrol, being very careful that no little thing was forgotten; for those little things can be so urgently wanted when unprocurable. A pack for every horse and mule, every pack arranged so that the articles needed from time to time could be got at quickly and easily without disturbing the rest of the pack. Numerous were the details that must first be attended to. Fitzer well knew the organization and efficiency needed to keep in smoothly running order a long and difficult patrol.

And the natives watching around the little police station kept Deven informed of every movement.

The *Maroubra* steamed up river and tied up to the little jetty at the depot. She commenced unloading her stores just as the patrol was ready to move off. The patrol rode away to the crossing.

The *Maroubra* unloaded within the next two or three days. Skipper Hales waved cheery farewell to Mrs Shadforth and the half-dozen station men gathered there, then moved away on the return journey downstream.

And hidden in the *Maroubra* were Bul-bul and tracker Splinter.

CHAPTER XII

NEMARLUK WALKS INTO THE TRAP

"THEY come!" grunted Deven, and his fierce eyes stared out into the night. Nemarluk and he were seated upon Deven's look out. Away below them the broad river mysterious under starlight stretched in a back line to right and left, the cliffs vanishing into blackness. Many miles away up river a red star twinkled. A signal fire upon a cliff.

"It is the signal," nodded Deven. "The patrol has crossed the river and is heading this way. It will be three days before they arrive here. You have no need to cross the river until the evening of the third day."

Nemarluk grunted. With a sliver of sandstone he was slowly sharpening his favourite spear blade.

"You will send word to Tiger to come?"

"To-morrow. When you lead the police away Tiger and I will follow in their tracks one day afterwards. Tiger can send word to Chugulla to bring along his men."

Even as they watched far back up there in the darkness the little *Maroubra* was chugging away down river with the tide, for the open sea and Darwin. She passed the black camps in the dead of night and felt the rise of the waves in Blunder Bay. Among the treacherous waters she felt her way along like a grey ghost in the night. Presently, her engines quietened as she neared a black shore. A dinghy was quietly lowered overside; unseen, it disappeared towards shore. Presently the dinghy returned, was hauled aboard,

and the *Maroubra* proceeded on her way towards
Queen's Channel and the open sea.

On the black shore two tall aboriginals stood, silent
as shadows.

The white's of Bul-bul's eyes glared at the gleam
in Splinter's eyes. Bul-bul laughed silently. Splinter
grinned reply. Invisible among the shadows of the
trees they cautiously began walking up river.

A magnificent type of a man, this Bul-bul; strong
as a lion, daring and quick in action, cunning as the
serpent. Splinter was a strong man, too, but wiry, with
the wonderful endurance of the aboriginal. Noiseless
as black panthers they vanished upstream.

Next night life went on as usual at the native camp.
The stockboys came in as usual to meet the wild bush
visitors, who constantly come and go. Women were
roasting bandicoot, possum, tortoise, and yam. Young
girls were pounding tamarind pods, to make the fruit
into a bitter jelly. A young tribesman with set face was
monotonously blowing the didjeridoo; its hoarse
blast swept out over the flat country and across the
river. An owl hooted from the river trees and was
echoed by its distant mate. Somewhere out in the
night a wild goose trumpeted, the call mellow with
distance.

A shaggy man glanced up inquiringly. His eyes
gleamed in the firelight as he bent to the coals, listening. Again there came that faint trumpet of the wild
goose calling to her mate. The man was gnawing a
bone but his ears were tensed. He felt a deathly chill
at his heart, the premonition of the aboriginal. That
trumpet call was to mean his death.

The life and laughter of the camp went serenely on.
No one had noticed the wild goose call; there were

plenty such calls from the mysterious night. The shaggy man was gnawing thoughtfully, enjoying his bone.

Deven squatted by a fire with Nemarluk. Around them squatted Deven's men, savage warrior every man, quick of eye and quick with spear. They were listening to Deven's low talk, their brows frowning, their eyes suspicious as they glanced around from beneath lowering brows. Pity help any one whom they detected listening-in.

But the groups around the dull fires were very discreet. All intent on their own business of gossiping, or corroboree singing, or spear-making. Or, like the shaggy man, quietly gnawing a bone.

Then the trumpet call came again. After a while the man threw the bone to his dog; spat thoughtfully; scratched his head; grasped his spears; stood up, and walked quietly out into the night. No tribesman walks out into the night without his spears, even for a few yards away. Who can tell that a painted enemy, agent of a vendetta, may not be waiting out there in the dark.

Once well away from the camp, the shaggy man hurried to the river stepped into a canoe and started softly paddling towards the opposite shore. It was a long way across but there was none to see that canoe steadily gliding over the water. The man sighed as he grounded the canoe and noiselessly stepped ashore. Bul-bul stood before him.

"So my totem brother answers," said Bul-bul softly.

"Yes. I heard the wild goose call."

"It is well."

They stared at one another, Splinter standing silently by.

"Where does Nemarluk land when he crosses the

river to escape from the white police?" demanded Bul-bul.

The shaggy one stared in sudden fear.

"Where does he land?" demanded Bul-bul.

"It means death if I tell," whispered the man.

"We will protect you."

"No one can protect me from the vengeance of Deven's men."

"They will never know."

"They know everything."

"Where does Nemarluk land?" insisted Bul-bul harshly. "I demand in the name of our totem."

"I will show you," mumbled the shaggy one at last. And the life had gone out of his voice.

He took them farther up river and pointed out the sheltered little cove to which Nemarluk usually guided his log with the tide.

"That is well," growled Bul-bul. "You have been true to the totem law. Return now, before they miss you." And the shaggy one stepped back into the canoe without answer. They stood there until long after he had vanished upon the river. Then Bul-bul chuckled softly.

"We have got our man," he hissed, his eyes gleaming with delight. "Come, we will hide." And they crept away.

Next morning Nemarluk crossed the river. He strode on into the bush with a smile upon his face, a song upon his lips. He took his time; he had plenty.

Two hours later Bul-bul was upon his tracks.

They fell upon him while he slept. He writhed up with steel upon his wrist, with Bul-bul's arm around his throat, with Splinter clinging to his waist, with the totem brother snatching at his ankles. They rolled over and over with Nemarluk roaring like a bull, clawing, biting. He upended Bul-bul and kicked the totem brother flat and gouged his thumb in Splinter's eye. But Bul-bul clung to the handcuffs, again they threw themselves upon him but he hurled them to earth except Bul-bul still clinging to the handcuffs. Panting like the savages they were they threw him down again while he snapped at Splinter's throat. They bore him to earth yet again and snarling as they fought, rolled over and over like a pack of dogs. Bul-bul suddenly jammed Nemarluk's head under a leaning root, then levered up his arm and snapped on the other cuff. They sprawled across him then, spitting blood from their crushed lips, panting their triumph.

Bul-bul and Splinter took him all the way back to Timber Creek. The totem brother disappeared, he had a long, long trip before him. He had greased and painted himself so that in the darkness he felt certain his own mother could never have recognized him. The job over, he fled in the darkness, fled as a man flees who knows that doom is on his tracks.

On the way up river they cut the tracks of a hunting party going out on to the plains. Bul-bul stared down, and grinned. He recognized every track, and one track there was of a man he wanted.

"Good hunting," he laughed to Splinter and Nemarluk. "It's a fine day; we'll do a little hunting too."

And he cast about for a hiding place. They lay in wait then for the return of the hunting party. They quite effectually gagged Nemarluk, Nemarluk with his hands manacled. Bul-bul left Splinter with a spear ready to hurl into Nemarluk's belly, while he walked away looking for something. He grinned as he measured it carefully, it was a round stick of hardwood and Bul-bul made certain it was small enough to fit in Nemarluk's jaws but large enough to defy his strong teeth. Nemarluk could accept the gag or not, just as he liked. Bul-bul would hold his nostrils until he decided. Hence, the furious Nemarluk could not warn the hunting party.

The hunting party returned, singing their way back to the river. The trackers sprang out upon the astonished Pundek, rolled him to the ground, and slipped the steel upon his wrists. Open-mouthed he gazed up at the grinning face of Bul-bul. Splinter grinned too, Splinter never did say much.

"A good hunt," grinned Bul-bul. "I see you've caught big game"—and he nodded to a kangaroo dropped by the startled men who had run on recognizing the trackers.

Pundek snarled.

"I'll go hunting big game one day," he hissed, "hunting a big, dingo-livered tracker!"

Bul-bul laughed as at a great joke. "Watch out it's not the hunter hunted," he roared, "as happened to-day."

"It will mean a spear in Bul-bul's kidneys," snarled Pundek. "You'll never catch me again."

"Bah!" sneered Bul-bul, "you couldn't hit a sleeping man on the head with a tomahawk!"

And Pundek writhed to break the handcuffs. For he was the one who had attempted to chop Constable Kennett to pieces.

But Pundek could not break the handcuffs. Panting, he glared into their interested, grinning faces, then relapsed into sullenness.

"Come!" ordered Bul-bul sharply, "it's over. All we've got to do now is to cage the bold, bad men."

And then Pundek saw the fierce eyes of Nemarluk. Nemarluk with steel upon his wrists. Pundek stared as Nemarluk spat out chips from the wood he had gnawed, spitting and chewing as if he were chewing the bones of Bul-bul.

"When you've finished your meal," grinned Bul-bul, "we'll get a move on."

Nemarluk cursed him as only an aboriginal can curse. Then they moved on swiftly; Bul-bul was taking no chances at an attempted rescue. He pressed them urgently forward to get as near Timber Creek as possible before Deven heard the news.

Fearfully, yet curiously, Nemarluk stared amongst the timber as they drew near Timber Creek. Soon he would be in the power of a white man policeman. He drew a long breath. Never had he dreamed that such a fate could befall him. Big, heavily timbered hills were all around them now. Soon they saw the dense timber of a river, the Shaw; the little iron police station peeping out from the timber; horses browsing near by. Then they heard the bark of a dog, and saw a tall young constable waiting. He stared at Nemarluk. Nemarluk stared back.

Bul-bul told his story. The policeman questioned him and Pundek. Then ordered food for the prisoners, with clothes and a blanket. By and by a tracker gave them each a pipe and tobacco. Both prisoners grinned hugely. This was not too bad at all.

Several days later Nemarluk drew a great breath. For here came Tiger, walking beside Bul-bul. Tiger, in white man's clothes. Tiger the cunning, watching this outpost of the whites. Tiger, whose savage face showed no sign.

Tiger was accused of killing the two white men, Cook and Stephens, who had left the Victoria River so many months ago. Tiger denied it. And they could not move him.

Hoping to draw him out, they then accused Nemarluk. Nemarluk laughed.

They could do nothing with Tiger. All the same they were very suspicious. It was the secret service at Bul-bul's command that at last had whispered of the killings.

"There will be a bit of tongue cutting for Deven in this!" thought Nemarluk. He gritted his teeth, glaring around. Pundek glared too, then struggled with expressionless eyes. For the time being at least, there could be no escape.

Another young policeman arrived, Constable Langdon from Brook's Creek, away inland behind Darwin. He was returning to Darwin in a few days and the prisoners would go with him. Nemarluk whispered of escape.

"If we can," whispered Pundek. "Watch out for any chance."

But there came no chance. The constable was too alert; he took no chances.

Nemarluk and his low-browed fellow prisoners walked all the way beside the police horses through bush to Darwin. Some hundreds of miles and into strange country, the country away behind the ranges which was foreign to Nemarluk. As day followed day his spirits sank. As mile followed mile every step became misery, a misery that took him farther and farther away from his own beloved country that he knew so well. Wildly he glanced around at the unfamiliar hills, the unknown flats, the strange timber, the creeks and gullies leading—where? He lay awake night after night quietly working at the steel chain. It was unbreakable.

Every night the policeman carefully examined the prisoners, to see they had picked up no stones with their feet during the day, and had neither wire nor iron nor similar aid to escape in their shaggy hair and beards; to make sure they had nothing with which, by patient labour night after night they might by "tap-tap-tapping" wear away a link in the chain.

Nearer the returning patrol drew to civilization, nearer, nearer.

Meanwhile, at Timber Creek Tiger had vanished—to meet Deven away up on the eyrie. There they whispered by the fire at night, and their eyes glowed fiercely as the eyes of a tigress who has lost her cubs.

Then, with all due regard to symbolic meaning, they oiled their bodies; painted them in the age-old custom with the terrifying marks of the killer, he who is on vengeance bent. A witch doctor came and crooned with them in a deep gorge, hour after hour going through the ceremonies.

At last, one night they crossed the Victoria. No one saw them go. No one whispered. Silently they vanished into the Wild Lands, seeking the tracks of the totem brother.

Far across plains and range and swamp, past Nemarluk's country even, on inland to the Daly. There, where he had sought shelter under the very noses of the whites, they caught him—and cut him to pieces.

Meanwhile, the returning patrol reached the little railway line which runs inland from Darwin. The constable breathed a sigh of relief. His dangerous prisoner, the man who had given the north so much trouble, was nearly caged.

And now Nemarluk rode on the little railway. When the tiny engine whistled he nearly jumped from his skin. The trackers grinned, then roared with laughter. The train puffed on. Nemarluk, squatted there holding on tight, was filled with a voiceless wonder. He stared at the hills running past, stared at the telegraph poles running past. He was as excited as a child when he saw a motor truck. Then there came this town of the white men set upon the harbour. Nemarluk just gazed—gazed at the town, the few streets, the people, at a steamer coming into the harbour. They took him from the train, through the town. At the sight of a big wall before him, a sudden premonition sent a chill to his heart. As they marched towards a gate in that wall he glared wildly around.

The big gate swung open. Nemarluk and his fellow prisoners shuffled in. The gate shut. Strong bolts shot into place.

Nemarluk was caged.

CHAPTER XIII

THE ESCAPE

WHEN put in a cell, the heart went out of Nemarluk;
he was a trapped animal. But it was not for very long.
One morning he was taken out and introduced to the
exercise yard.

A huge yard with brilliant sunlight above, a towering wall all around. He stood there gazing. But soon
his lined face took on the old boyish grin. His Red
Band, Minmara and Marragin, Mankee and Mangul
and Lin, were there grinning. He laughed as they
crowded around him. Outlaws from the Brinken were
grinning from across the yard, a Mulluk-Mulluk cattle
spearer he knew was grinning from the woodyard,
quite a number of renegades he knew well were
grinning towards him. Suddenly he felt almost at
home. Strangers from unknown tribes grinned towards him as they worked, drawn together in the
comradeship of captivity. Many came towards him.

He was a hero.

At first, he dreaded the white jailers. But they were
good to him, keenly interested in this big native outlaw of whom the patrol men spoke so often.

They gave him wonderful food, warm blankets, even
tobacco. It was not long before he was strolling around
the yard as though he owned the place.

In Fanny Bay Jail Nemarluk met many a warrior
famous in aboriginal story. Powerful men from the
wilds of Arnhem Land, wiry little men from the
desert lands far back in the interior, broad-chested
men from the coastal islands, bushmen from the forest

land. He had never dreamed his country was such a big place, nor that it held so many tribes. He had not even heard of the majority of the tribes represented here.

These men were the killers of white men, of aboriginal, of Japanese, of Malay. Among them were cattle spearers and camp raiders who had led the police many a long chase. Fascinating stories were told as these men swapped experiences, each boasting of the way he had deceived police and trackers, or cattlemen, pearlers, or miners,

Nemarluk loved listening to these stories; he would laugh loud and long. Sometimes, though, the laugh died on his face as a bird flew swiftly by overhead. At such times he could smell the leaves from the jungle just outside the jail yard. Above, was the open sky.

Four months went by. Then, one night Nemarluk heard faintly, the trumpet call of a wild goose. It was speeding far up in the night, on free wings sailing swiftly for the Wild Lands far away. Nemarluk could not sleep.

Breathlessly, he lay awake, his eyes staring at the blackness of prison walls. He listened, listened, for hours. Faintly, very faintly he believed he heard the deep, droning note of the didjeridoo. He moaned; he was sure he heard that didjeridoo two hundred miles away. The darkness was making tiny hissing noises like the whispering of spirits. It seemed to him he could smell the gum blossoms, the tide coming in over the mud flats. Were the spirits whispering to him? Or could he really hear the bats chattering in the blossom laden branches? A possum screeching in a fig-tree? He tossed over and again lay still, his eyes staring into the darkness. A rat was with him, its teeth plainly chewing something in the corner. He hardly heard it; his ears were straining to catch sounds far, far away, he felt he could have sacrificed his liberty to hear the hoot of a boobook owl. Ah! from now the white gums would shed their bark; the bamboo thickets along the Daly would soon sprout in juicy green; the crocodiles would nest and lay in cool lagoons.

Next morning he was allowed out to do his easy work in the exercise yard. But his smile held a hidden meaning; his eyes were furtive; he had never worked so willingly; he sang as he worked each time a white jailer went by. There came spell-oh time. The prisoners drifted away from their tasks to spell in little squatting groups around the yard, joking and yarning as usual. But now they were—plotting!

Escape!

"The gate!" whispered Longlegs. Longlegs the cunning, he and Kalomy were here now charged with the killing of James Nichols. Minmara glanced towards the gate, they all glanced towards the gate. Then gazed at one another then quickly went on yarning, to laugh uproariously as Lin cracked a joke. Nemarluk felt his spear hand trembling. Oh, if only he had a weapon.

At the back of the jail exercise yard there was a gate, and this was opened every morning while men carried out the garbage tins to a waiting truck outside. Only one jailer stood guard by this gate.

"We will rush him!" whispered Nemarluk. "All together, to-morrow morning. Will you follow me?"

They nodded, and went on with their work.

All that long day Nemarluk could plainly smell the scent of trees, of sea water not far away. There seemed to be a humming in his ears; there was a thumping at his heart; his eyes could hardly leave the sky.

That night, his face changed. His eyes glared, he breathed deeply into the darkness, his ears listened for sounds impossible to hear within caged walls. He listened, listened, listened. The fierce expression of the animal man crept into his face. Nemarluk was not laughing now.

Next morning they were marched as usual into the exercise yard, the jail routine went on. When the time came the gate creaked open, sunlight streamed in, Nemarluk heard the call of birds from the jungle-scrub just beyond the walls. His lips were parted, his eyes glaring madly. The garbage tins were now being carried out. The prisoners engaged on their different tasks began to edge nearer the gate. The jailer supervising the removal of the garbage did not notice, all was as usual.

Suddenly Namarluk hurled himself at the jailer and both men crashed. Nemarluk was up and away as the jailer rose to his knees whipped out his revolver and fired, then sprang up and faced the excited crowd surging upon him.

"Back! Back!" he cried. "Back or I fire!"

They hesitated at that revolver now within inches of them, glared at the determined face of the shouting man behind the gun. Other jailers came running. Sullenly the prisoners were forced back into the yard.

Nemarluk leaped a fence, was in the jungle-scrub and away. He took to the water. Instead of making straight back for the wilds he travelled the mangrove country half way around Darwin harbour, eighty miles of nightmare. Weaponless, he would have tackled any one who attempted to stop him. He snarled; he felt he could tear a man to pieces with hands and teeth. But in that eighty-mile labyrinth of mangrove and mud and water he met no one. He emerged among the sand-dunes and scrubs at Talc Head, straight across the harbour, right opposite Darwin.

His sleek body scatched and torn and covered with mud, his eyes staring from his head as a wild man again as he glared towards the camp fires of the local native camp. He sneered contemptuously. Tame natives these, used to working occasionally for white men, to canoeing across the harbor to sneak into the white man town at night. He sprang into the camp and seized the nearest bundle of spears. In an instant he was threatening them.

The people squatted there, cowed.

"Nemarluk!" cried a woman.

At that dreaded name they never moved. He laughed harshly, snatched a fish from the coals and wolfed it. He seized another, then another, he ate as a famished man. Then he went around the camp and examined every weapon. He selected the best wommera, the best knife, and the best six spears. Then snarled at them:

"He who betrays Nemarluk I will kill."

He glared at them, then vanished.

But not out of earshot of the camp. Should it be raided, he wanted to hear. Working his way among clumps of bamboo and thickets of vine scrub, he came to a steep, scrub-lined embankment. He gazed up, and slowly grinned. A man could sleep safetly away up there. He who sought him must climb up and get him. The next day Nemarluk pointed out a bamboo thicket to the local tribe:

"In there I sleep," he grunted, "and if any man enter there while I sleep he will feel my spear."

But from his real sleeping place he could see by day across the harbour the white roof of the police station and government buildings on Darwin headlands. Could see the pearling luggers at anchor, could see any movement upon the harbour. No police boat appeared upon the harbour. Nemarluk was waiting for his men —and Marboo. She was captive in the women's compound. He thought surely some of the men must have escaped, he had fled on the wings of the wind when the jailer fired at him and did not know what had happened behind. But surely some must have followed him to scatter and hide in the surrounding bush. Surely he would hear gossip of such from these local people. If only some men had escaped and could all join up together he had a hazy idea of attempting to rescue Marboo. And then . . .

But the police had guessed. They set a trap for him, but Nemarluk never came.

No aboriginal warrior worthy of the name will fly away and leave his woman—if he can possibly help it.

It was a fortnight before the local tribe quietly sent word across the water.

A black night came. It was after midnight.

A tiny boat sailing quietly across the harbour, sailing towards Talc Head. Constable Don, and trackers Smiler and Gilly. A quiet, determined man this tracker Smiler. A tall man, thin and a fighter.

Silently they beached their boat, and vanished into the scrub.

Steel grey of dawn. Very cold, Nemarluk in uneasy sleep coiled up beside his spears. He dared not light a fire.

Suddenly Nemarluk awoke as a startled animal awakes. Spears in hand he peered through the bushes then crept out. Up over the rim of the embankment appeared a head, a tracker's head, a thin face from which stared piercing eyes. Then the tall body of tracker Smiler leaped up on top. Both men glared, then each came at the other.

"Stand! Stand!" called Smiler and fired as Nemarluk threw. The revolver barrel just flicked the spear and it grazed Smiler's singlet on the left side. Again he parried and the second spear grazed his right side.

They were at one another's throats then, Smiler desperately gripping Nemarluk's spear arm while Nemarluk was wrenching at the revolver. Panting and gasping they swayed there while Nemarluk's greater weight slowly forced Smiler back, back, back. Nemarluk's eyes were glaring their triumph into Smiler's face, who felt his back was breaking, when he wrenched away his arm and crashed his revolver butt on Nemarluk's head. To a gasping grunt Nemarluk heaved forward and both men went crashing down the embankment.

Nemarluk was up in an instant and running for his own country, far away.

Calling on his great reserve of strength Nemarluk hurried on through bush day and night, making for the Daly River. Once across the river he would speed on into the safety of the Wild Lands.

When nearing the Daly, he was almost dead-beat. In all these many miles he had not seen a soul, nor track of black man or white. Fiercely he pushed on, into a wild night. Hungry for sight of camp fires, for corroboree song, for his own people. The thought of An-de-mallee camp, of In-dar-roo, filled him with renewed strength. He pressed on. He would get news of his people from the tribesmen at the Daly, the men of the Mulluk-Mulluk and Brinken would surely know. He could hide along the Daly, eat and rest and sleep, then push on into his own beloved country. Collect his tribal people around him and travel on into the Moyle and the Fitzmaurice. Join up with Tiger and Chugulla and the warriors of Tiger's Mob. Send word for Deven's men to join them. And then—Nemarluk gritted his teeth and pushed on—and then—he would get Bul-bul.

There came the cool loneliness of the night. Stars peeped out, black shadows lay upon the hills; shadows too in gully and ravine and among clumps of trees. Cautiously now Nemarluk pushed on, listening for the distant yelp of a dog, for the drone of the didgeridoo. They could not be far away now. But only the silence of the night came to him.

With eyes, ears, nostrils—every sense—alert, Nemarluk struggled on. He could hardly push the leaden feeling out of his legs now; he felt weak from strain and loss of sleep and hunger, lonely and savage as a hunted wolf.

He did not know that only that very morning word had arrived from distant Darwin of Nemarluk's escape. The constable in charge of the little Daly River outpost immediately made ready to raid the native camp. He felt sure Nemarluk would make straight back for his own country and would call at the camp. Silently constable and trackers stepped out into the night.

It was almost dawn when Nemarluk drew near the camp. He crouched, then knelt, listening. Not a sound. After a while he crouched forward again, kneeling now as he came closer and closer. He listened . . . Not a murmur. The people would be soundly asleep for these were the heavy hours when the aboriginal sleeps soundest. . . . Nemarluk could wait no longer. He stepped towards the camp.

A shadow rose from just ahead and glided towards the camp. Nemarluk crouched with wildly beating heart. His staring eyes saw another shadow rise and crouch forward towards the camp.

Nemarluk waited, his heart thumping wildly. Suddenly there was a rush from all sides upon the camp. Alarmed scream of a woman, yelp of dogs, men jumping up to startled yells.

Nemarluk turned and ran back then doubled around the camp and ran, ran, ran.

He ran until long after sunup. Ran until he fell exhausted. He crept into a bamboo thicket; his head fell upon his arms and he slept.

A week later Nemarluk reached An-de-mallee camp.

With his people around him he ate and slept, just ate and slept. He lazed away the days, resting and making new spears; telling the people of the dangers he had been through, of the wonders of Darwin town, of the big jail and the great men he had met there. He spread their names around; boasted of their deeds, the deeds of the cattle spearers and the killers. Eagerly they listened. They could not hear enough; many of these deeds would be sung in corroboree at the next ceremonies. Eagerly Mangul's people and they of Mankee and Lin and Minmara and Marragin, all the people of the Red Band, asked for news of their boys, for more news and still more news.

People from other tribes began drifting in to learn news of their men now held in the white man's jail. Nemarluk by day and around the fires at night had an audience he could not satisfy.

He felt wonderfully happy; sometimes the camp would even echo to his old boyish laugh. Away back here in the Wild Lands among friends again he felt safe. He swore to be avenged for his Red Band prisoners in faraway Darwin jail. Fiercely he swore he would never be taken again.

They received a smoke signal with news from away towards the Victoria River. The news warned of police patrols, seeking Tiger's Mob.

"They will never catch Tiger!" said Nemarluk savagely.

But one evening a runner came panting into camp.

"They've caught Chugulla!"

"Chugulla!" exclaimed Nemarluk.

"Yes. And Uninyah, too."

"Who caught him?" demanded Nemarluk. And he knew the answer.

"Bul-bul caught him."

Nemarluk gripped his favourite spear.

"They have put iron on Chugulla," went on the messenger. "They force him to take them to Tiger's hideout."

Nemarluk frowned. But the messenger roared laughing.

"Chugulla is taking them a walk. They will walk until they drop. But—they won't find Tiger."

He seized the leg of a half-roasted wallaby on the fire, wrenched the leg from the body, and ate ravenously.

CHAPTER XIV

BUL-BUL

NEMARLUK with his people started out for the Moyle
country where now the game was plentiful. Here they
would hunt while practising for the Big Corroborees
soon due, when all the tribes would gather for the
initiation ceremonies. Here, far away from the police,
they would meet Tiger's Mob.

But Tiger was too cunning; he guessed a patrol
would soon visit the Big Ring Corroboree camp. With
his henchman, Wadawarry, he had doubled away to
the Daly River. Here, right under the nose of the Daly
Police Outpost, he believed the police would never
expect him. With Chugulla on leash, Constables Fitzer
and Langton were patrolling the Victoria River
country.

At the thought of Chugulla, skinny old Alligator
laughed. Squatting there with hunched shoulders, his
knees under his chin, he looked like a long, half-
starved, leering crane. Walung and big Chalmer,
Chin-amon and the sullen Maru, all laughed over the
camp fires as day by day the tribes congregated from
far and wide.

"It's such a pleasant walk Chugulla is leading them,"
said Alligator, with his leering grin, "into all the bogs
he can find, then into the roughest country in the foothills. Then he brings them out into the scrubs where
all the prickly vines are. And that big dingo Bul-bul
must take step by step with him. Ha! ha! ha!"

"I saw one policeman with his tongue hanging out
for a drink of water," grinned Walung. "The other

was twenty miles away trying to bring the horses around a bog. You couldn't see horses or men for mud."

"That would have been the time to have speared them!" declared Nemarluk.

"Yes," agreed Chin-amon, "had we been all together. But Tiger had doubled back to the Daly. Chugulla was a prisoner. One half of us were dogging the policeman and trackers with the horses, the other half were dogging the other policeman and Bul-bul with Chugulla."

"I wish I'd been there," frowned Nemarluk, "with you and with Deven's men."

"Ah!" said Mara, "we would have speared them all. But if you were dogging them now you'd find they were wideawake. The trackers are scared for their lives; and they know Chugulla is leading them a dance."

"May he wear their feet out," grinned Nemarluk. "May their bones for ever stay in the mud."

"Wah!" boomed Chalmer. And there was no laughter in the giant's face.

"Tiger was away on the Daly," smiled Nemarluk, "the police away back towards the Victoria chasing a phantom, and we here at the Big Ring camp. What a scatter! And we're quite safe."

"If they come while we're at the ceremonies," snarled Walung, "there'll be trouble."

Fiercely they swore to back him up. Nemarluk was happy and excited. This year the Great Ceremonies would be held. After the ceremonies the tribes would disperse. The police by then would be weary travelling the country looking for them here, there, everywhere. While they were in a muddle he and Tiger's Mob and Deven would get together and plan—and act. He clenched his fist, his eyes gleaming. Soon now Nemarluk the chief would be the hunter, not the hunted.

"Would you like to hunt a patrol?" he hissed to Chalmer.

"Big game, that!" boomed the giant. "But I'll hunt anything."

"He! he! he!" piped Alligator. "Just fancy Bul-bul with a spear through his ribs in the night."

"He'd twist about like a stuck snake," gloated Maru. "I hope my spear does it."

"It shall be mine!" hissed Nemarluk.

"Looks as if Walung and me and the others will have to spear the policemen on our own," grinned Chin-amon. "Deven's men don't like Bul-bul either."

"Cut Charlie's kidneys out for me," called Kergutt. "I want his fat to grease my axe."

"You shall have it!" promised Pooneemillar. And they laughed.

Kergutt was the lame one. A bullet had done it, a bullet from Charlie the tracker's rifle as he writhed with a spear in his leg. Kergutt had been very lame ever since. He had been a great runner, not one of his tribe could run down game as he could. He would never run again. Now he sat by the fire, grinding his axe blade with sand. Very patient he was, making a good job of it. He had securely fixed the axe head in a wooden haft, then lashed them together with boab-tree fibre, firmly embedded in bees-wax, hardened gum and native resin. He wanted Charlie's kidney fat to grease the lashings.

"I can make it last a long time," he said as he bent over the axe. "I can melt every little bit into oil that will keep my axe handle strong throughout many a wet season."

"You want to have Charlie always with you," grinned Chalmer.

"Yes," answered Kergutt, as thoughtfully he thumbed the blade. "I want to smell him beside me as I sleep at night."

But although Nemerluk was fiercely anxious for a clash with the patrols he had learned to respect the police. He had learned never to take a chance. And now, with so many people around, he chose a safe sleeping place. Amongst the gathering tribes there would be those defiant of Nemarluk now that his Red Band was gone. Besides, the ceaseless vendettas of tribal life would be quietly carried on. No aboriginal is ever quite free of the fear of vendetta. So in the dead of night Nemarluk would glide from all the people, and in a safe place sleep alone.

In the forest country now the women easily found the dark green stalks and leaves of the big yam. Out on the plains, battalions of brolgas were trumpeting and dancing. All the swamps were alive with noisy waterfowl, with black duck and the whistler, with many other ducks and the black and white geese and the piping geese, with the cackling water-hen, with herons and cranes from the tiny one to the long-stepping, solemn giant, tall as a man. In creek bank and lagoon bank were the freshly dug holes of king-fisher, of water-rat and turtle. The big water-rat which sneaks out at night and bites like a fury if cornered, the "dry" land turtle and the Ngart, that big river turtle, and the little Bandak turtle of the orange-striped eye.

Fat tree snakes slithered among the foliage above, while in the water the small Johnson-river crocodile with many young ones was basking among the waterlilies. The silver perch were fat, all the fish were fat, the fresh-water shell-fish were fat.

And Nature's primitive children grew fat on this plentiful game. Day by day now clouds of wildfowl, clouds of shrieking cockatoos and parrots told where the people were hunting. At sundown distant "Yak-aing" told of the hunters coming home from all points of the compass, like the birds returning to roost. Away across the big camping grounds many fires then would start up as tribe after tribe came straggling in and made ready for the evening feast. Corroboree songs and dances made happy the nights.

One night the crowds gathered round to hear a story and stamp in rage at the police. Far away, Chugulla was still leading them a dance. Chugulla and Uninyah had planned to escape, leaving the patrol in the heart of a morass. They were on a chain. All that day, in a land in which water was plentiful, Chugulla had guided the patrol where water was not. A long, tiring, hot march. At sundown the weary patrol camped; men and animals could hardly drag one leg after the other. Tracker Torung was ordered to escort Chugulla and Uninyah away, and find clear water near camp. Sullenly the two prisoners and tracker disappeared among the bushes. The suspicious Bul-bul picked up a spear and quietly followed them. And in a lonely place he saw the two prisoners suddenly wheel around and throw the tracker to the ground. Like tigers they were upon him, throttling the life out of him. Bul-bul leaped straight through the bushes, and jabbed Chugulla with the spear. Then jabbed Uninyah hard. He laughed at them.

The messenger looked around at the great circle of staring eyes. The people had hung on his every word.

K

The warriors snarled; a totem brother of Uninyah chewed his beard in rage. Chugulla's nephew leaped up, rattling his spears and shrieking. Warriors jumped up to stamp in the vengeance dance as the women chanted blood-curdling song, drumming their thighs. Just let these people lay their hands on Bul-bul and see who would laugh then!

The dance that night was fast and furious, boiling with the lust for vengeance.

Nemarluk was in his glory among these tribes of the Wild Lands during these seasonal ceremonies: leader of the hunt among all the people, leader of the ceremonies. It is only the strong and the cunning who can hold power among primitive people. Nemarluk well knew that among all these tribes he really was not nearly so powerful now, because of the loss of his fighting Red Band. But he bluffed this out by boasting what he would do when Tiger's Mob and Deven's men joined together, after the ceremonies. He would lead them against the white police. He shouted his threat before them all, in the centre of the circle, before the Council of the Old Men.

And the people, outlined by the flames of the ceremonial fires, roared approval; squad after squad of tribesmen came stamping into the circle to dance their threat of vengeance.

But a jealous few squatted quietly watching, saying nothing. They would wait and see.

And the moon rose to throw silver light on savage dancers, in painted bars of yellow and white on black bodies, bounding into the firelight, stamping and hissing with eyes animal mad and faces distorted in the red light of the flames. Shrieking like devils they leaped through the ceremonial flames and with one great stamp suddenly stood motionless.

Secure there in the heart of the Wild Lands with hundreds of warriors around him, Nemarluk flung himself into the spirit of the ceremonies and almost forgot the white police.

He was rudely awakened.

From a distant crag a smoke signal arose. Tiger had been captured!

That afternoon as from far and wide the hunting bands came into the main camp, Tiger's name was on every lip. And every one was watching—Nemarluk! And Tiger's men, too: Old Alligator and the giant Chalmer, and Chin-amon and Walung and Maru. Low-browed, sullen, they squatted there. Squatted apart around their own fire, in low gutturals talking seriously. Their weapons were close around them, a snarl upon their lips. Just one loose remark from all those people so obviously minding their own business —just one covert sneer—and the spears of these men would fly to their mark.

They could hardly believe the news. Tiger the cunning, Tiger the fighter, Tiger the unbeaten warrior who so passionately had sworn he would never be taken alive. And they had believed him!

"Treachery!" hissed Nemarluk. And the eyes of the hunted band glanced around at the black groups of people around many a fire.

The full moon made beautiful the water-lily swamps lined with their tall, white paper-barks. Pink flames crinkled the water; loaned pink dresses to the trunks of the paper-barks. A possum screeched suddenly, a nankin bird cackled harshly.

"Treachery!" hissed Nemarluk again.

"Is the man born who would risk the wrath of Tiger?" grunted Walung.

"There must be!" snarled Maru. "Otherwise how

did the police know he had slipped back to the Daly?"

"Wadjee is watching us!" hissed Alligator as he bent towards the fire. The morose face of Maru broke into a snarl. They all stared sullenly at the fire except Nemarluk. He glared defiantly around; he would have torn the throat out of the dreaded witch doctor even, had he been sure the cunning terror was intriguing against him.

Old Wadjee, the witch doctor, squatted by his fire, apart from all, with his painted skull, his bag of charms, his Death Bone beside him.

But it was not the witch doctor who had betrayed Tiger. It was Tiger's wife. She hated him; he had been very cruel to her and had driven her away from the tribe. A few days ago she had been wandering with a quaint hill tribe, away back in the mountains. A little outcast tribe this, to which outcasts drifted. The police had raided the camp. Gladly then Tiger's wife stepped forward and shrieked her betrayal.

"Tiger has run to the Daly," she shrieked. "Catch him! Kill him!"

The patrol travelled fast by night, hid by day then travelled by night again. They caught Tiger and Wadawarry in their full war paint dancing in the madness of a war corroboree. Tiger fought like the tiger he was, but they bore him to earth and snapped the steel upon his wrists. Screaming his fury he bit up into the panting face of Bul-bul. Bul-bul held his throat just out of reach and laughed while Tiger writhed and spat up at him. And that was the news.

Uneasy days passed by. Away back in the Wild Lands at Meewa swamp, Nemarluk and Tiger's men held serious council.

"We must take to the hills!" frowned Nemarluk.

"Must we for ever run?" sneered Maru.

"Yes!" answered Nemarluk furiously—"until we are all together."

"There are enough of us here to eat them," growled Walung.

"Yes," replied Nemarluk, "if only they would bite. They won't. If I had my Red Band, if Tiger were here, if Deven were here, then all these hundreds would face the guns of the patrol."

"Nemarluk is right," said old Alligator seriously. "These corroboree warriors are all wind. If the police came galloping now these brave warriors would run like dingoes from their guns."

"You know it," frowned Nemarluk. "How many times have we tried to face our own tribesmen up to the patrols? Tiger has tried, and all who would back him up were you few men of Tiger's Mob. Deven has tried, but only Deven's men backed him up. I have tried, but only my Red Band were prepared to face the guns of the police. We have only one hope now. To collect what are left of Tiger's Mob then join with Deven. Only then will we have a chance; until then we must run."

"The ceremonies are due!" protested Chin-amon. "They may not come. We need not run until they are upon us!"

"Yes," said Chalmer eagerly, "let us wait at least until they do come. We can slip away then; they can never catch us."

"How often have we said, 'They will never catch us!'" frowned Nemarluk. "And look what they have caught! Half of the very best of us are gone. They caught me. They have even caught Tiger"

"Let us run then," growled Maru, "but not until they come. If we run now the people here will sneer

as soon as our backs are turned. They will say we run
from the police; always run, run, run."

"That is so," frowned Nemarluk. "Our enemies
grow bolder as we go under. Let us stay then, but stick
together; be ready any moment day or night to fly."

Uneasily they carried on with preparations to take
their part in the ceremonies.

One bright morning a shout arose. All stared
towards the distant ranges from which smoke signals
arose.

"The white police!" snarled Maru. "They come!"

"Let us go," grunted Nemarluk.

They made for the ranges.

And the next day Bul-bul was upon their tracks.

Day by day the big tracker patiently followed those
tracks, along valleys and over hills and even over long
rocky spurs, then into country impassable for horses.
Even after heavy rain he detected the shadowy impression upon wet grass where Chin-amon's body had lain.
Over a patch of hard country covered by rubble
pebbles he tracked them. Quite simply. Every here and
there he found a loose pebble that had been pushed
lightly into the ground. The foot of a heavy man,
travelling swiftly, would do that. Yet again, in heavily
grassed country his hawk's eyes noticed where a little
grass had been bent over, only just here and there,
a hundred yards or so apart. But the foot of a fleeing
man had done it.

Upon the bare rock that in some places lined the
crest of a ridge he got the sun behind him in a certain
way then squinted down and along the rock, his eyes
reading the hard, brown surface. And just here, just
there, he detected the shadow moisture left by a bare
foot. It is only the very best of trackers that can do

that. But it can be done, granted favourable weather conditions and the knowledge of how to do it. An expert tracker may detect that faint, ghostly film which may be left upon the hardened rock by a human foot.

When he lost their tracks he circled the last track in ever-widening circles until he found a tell-tale mark where they had come out on to softer country.

It was slow work but Bul-bul worked as sure as fate.

Days went by and he was still tracking. Then the tracks doubled back towards the open country. Bul-bul grinned, knowing that the hunted men thought they had lost their tracks in the ranges. The foot-walkers and the horsemen thus joined up again and the patrol rode on through the bush—on the tracks of the wanted men.

It was a beautiful day, fleecy clouds in a bright sky. The woollybutt blossoms scented the air. Bright-eyed honeysuckers busily dipped curved beaks into the blossoms, shooting their pointed tongues deep to the nectar. Shrieking parrots made gay with colour the flowering trees.

Squatting in the shade upon a dried-up marsh, Nemarluk and Chin-amon and Maru were eating lily roots and roasted tortoise and water-rats. This shallow little marsh had dried up very quickly, and upon its hard-baked surface fresh holes showed where the wild men had been digging mussels. There was plentiful food here, unlike the rocky ranges. They lay back full-bellied, dozing the morning away.

Upon a distant little hill away across on the edge of the marsh a black crow squatted. That crow was old Alligator the look-out man. In the warm sunlight he was nearly dozing too. Something made Alligator suspicious. He became an alert black sentinel—too late. With his shrill wail of alarm the thud of galloping hooves startled Nemarluk's men. They sprang up spears in hand, gazing wildly around. They saw horses charging from the trees as they galloped around the little hill.

Old Alligator was caught. Alligator who had witnessed the killing of the Japanese; had seen the killing of Cook and Stephens.

Nemarluk and Tiger's men vanished, travelling like the wind.

Fear chilled Nemarluk's heart. One by one he had lost his own Red Band. Devon has lost Kummungeegut, Kerinbo, Pooneemillar, and others of his very best men. Pundek was captive. Stockman Jimmy, who had killed the white man Tetlow, was caught. Then Chugulla was caught, and Uninyah; and now Tiger himself. One by one Tiger's Mob was going as his own Red Band had gone. Wadawarry already caught, and now in all probability Alligator.

"Are they everywhere?" snarled Maru as they ran. "Do they never sleep? Are they behind every rock, every tree? We think them a hundred miles away and they are right on our very heels. We think we have lost them, and they raid our camp with the dawn."

"Bul-bul is on our tracks," grunted Chin-amon.

And he was.

The hunted men snarled at Chin-amon's remark. They had no time to hide their tracks now, they must first put distance between them and that persistent patrol.

At sunset they hurried into a big camp of Fitzmaurice men. Angry warriors surrounded them as they told of their flight from the police. There was a

rattling of spears, fierce talk of fight, shrill urging by
the women. On the cooking stones were fish now
nearly cooked and many goose eggs and berries in
the hot ashes. After an angry talk they split up into
groups around the fires, but had hardly commenced to
eat when a shaggy man raised his head inquiringly.

Instant silence. Every eye stared; every nostril sniffed
the air.

Then the warriors snatched spears, and the whole
tribe, warriors, women, children, dogs, vanished into
the thickets.

They had smelt the salty tang of sweating horses.

Hardly minutes later the camp was raided.

Crouched in a dense thicket among all those listening people Nemarluk and his hunted men waited and
listened, then planned.

"They will ride away," whispered Nemarluk to
Maru and Chin-amon and Walung. "Though they
ride away they will hide their men in the camp. We
are children no longer to fall to such a trick. Towards
dawn we will slip away and make for the lily lagoon
as if hurrying for the hills. You lose your tracks in
the lagoon then make for Wah-wee hill; you can see
far over the country from there. I won't enter the
lagoon but will keep straight on as if we have decided
to split up. If they follow my tracks signal me later
from the hill; if they follow you, signal me; if they
split up and follow both you and me, signal also—
then lose yourselves. I think they'll follow me first.
I'll lead them in a chase that will cripple their horses
and themselves; take them right back to Victoria
River, then double back along the sea. There I'll lose
them, if I can't at the Victoria, and strike inland to
Meewa swamp. I'll meet you there at the new moon."

"A good plan," grunted Walung. "If they want to

catch all of us, we must split up. If they still chase us, we'll split up again, and yet again."

"We'll have them walking in circles all over the country," laughed Chin-amon.

"If only Tiger were here!" snarled Maru.

"If only I had my Red Band," hissed Nemarluk, "or if only Deven's men were with us, we could trap them and kill them one by one."

"We must strike at them soon," growled Maru, "or they'll have us scattered all over the country like flying dingoes."

"We dare not strike until we are all together," snarled Nemarluk. "We must make sure."

Before dawn Maru, Walung, and Chin-amon entered the lagoon.

"Ma-muck!" waved Nemarluk in farewell and strode on into the lightening day.

Surely enough, several hours later the watchers on Wah-wee hill saw horsemen following the fresh tracks. Bul-bul in the lead leaning over his horse's neck travelling at a fast walk. The fleeing men had made no attempt to disguise their tracks.

The patrol halted at the lagoon, Bul-bul pointed out Nemarluk's tracks leading away. The white policeman ordered him on and the patrol turned, hurrying on the tracks of Nemarluk. Chin-amon laughed.

"We've fooled them," grunted Walung. "After all, they are easy to fool."

"Wah!" frowned Maru. "Yet they are catching us one by one."

They squatted there until certain that all the patrol were hot on Nemarluk's tracks. Then signalled.

Nemarluk, miles away and heading towards the Victoria saw the smoke arising from Wah-wee hill. He shook his spears at the unseen patrol behind him, then set his mind not to hiding tracks, but to leading the pursuers over the worst country he could find. He set off at a tangent to strike a line of waterless country.

Chin-amon, Walung, and Maru hurried down from the hill and made straight back for the Fitzmaurice camp. They were very hungry. The people would be awaiting them, knowing that all were now safe. The patrol now would be twenty miles away, travelling farther away as Nemarluk led them on and on.

That night by the sleeping fires among their hundred tribesmen Chin-amon, Walung, and Maru slept soundly.

Just before dawn they awoke to the grip of hands. And steel was upon their wrists.

CHAPTER XV

THE FIGHT

It was midday, Nemarluk squatted behind a tufted bush, glaring back the way he had come. Broken country this but not high country. Around him were little rocky knolls to which clung patches of dwarf scrub. The drab yellow country in between was crisscrossed by dry ravines dotted with thorny shrubs. Coarse grasses grew in tufts between granite boulders shining under the sun. The broken ground was hot and parched. Nemarluk grinned. The patrol had dogged him for many, many miles. And now their legweary horses, nearly perishing with thirst, must battle on into country such as this. Behind the bushes upon this little rocky knoll he could see quite a distance back. He watched two cockatoos winging their way to water. They were flying steadily back over the country through which he had travelled. But the birds did not screech, did not swerve and fly lower as they would out of curiosity had they seen any unusual moving thing. The patrol must be a long way back.

The policeman, the trackers, must be very tired and dispirited. Except Bul-bul. Nemarluk's eyes gleamed fiendishly. It was Bul-bul he wished to ambush. To watch him coming on, on, on, along his tracks. To gaze on his bent head as he tracked right up to this very bush and then—to gaze an instant into his startled face as he buried his spear in his chest. Then to vanish among the rocks.

Suddenly, Nemarluk stared, gazing far away. He did not seem to breathe. A flock of squatter pigeons

walked almost past his feet. Their nuggety little bodies
were clothed in slaty brown like the earth upon which
they walked nearly in single file, solemn little birds,
bright-eyed; they love the warm earth. They vanished
amongst the tufted grasses.

Far away, Nemarluk was watching a smoke signal.
It told of the arrest of Walung and Chin-amon and
Maru.

Nemarluk sat with loneliness clutching his heart.
His Red Band gone, Tiger's Mob gone, he was alone
again. He thought of Marboo, far away.

At last he wondered at the cunning of the police
patrol. The policeman must have guessed that Nemarluk was a decoy. He must have followed in his tracks
until sundown then doubled back swiftly and raided
the Fitzmaurice camp with the dawn.

Nemarluk frowned with anxiety. No longer he scorned the endurance, the initiative, the cunning of the white police. They were always here, there, somewhere. Always coming, coming, coming. And now they would be after him alone: now he could never rest, never be safe.

His eyes glared as suddenly he took an amazed breath, staring back along his tracks. A painted warrior appeared. Then another and another, and two more. They were coming along his tracks, killer spears in their hands. Their bodies daubed in pipe clay and ochre, feather in their headbands, the scarlet band of the killer upon each painted brow.

Nemarluk almost sprang up, his heart thumping painfully. A vengeance party! Upon *his* tracks.

Such a band he knew, dare not again return to their tribe until they had accomplished their vengeance. Ah, Nemarluk, King of the Wilds, the hunted man! Where were his feared warriors of yesterday? Gone. And now some "dingo" of the hills had set a vengeance party upon his tracks. He was a doomed man. Drawing a great breath he gripped his spears. He had fine spears. Like a snake slithering to the earth he crept sideways and down into a ravine. Bent double, he ran swiftly back towards those oncoming men. Then paused, straightening up to peer through the bushes. Ah! they were just going past.

Fitting a spear to his wommera he drew steady breath, his face set grimly. He must not miss with one solitary spear. Noiselessly Nemarluk stood erect with spear arm balancing the long weapon. It flew from the wommera and the blade bit straight into the back of the last man. He screamed and leaped forward to crash down tearing at the grass. Nemarluk was bent double as he ran back along the ravine, his eyes tigerish, another spear ready in his hand. The avengers had scattered; one leaped down into the ravine. Nemarluk was upon him stabbing, stabbing, stabbing. Then he turned and doubled back again, leaped out of the ravine, dived across his own tracks, and crouched amongst the rocks. He was now behind the hunters.

Panting, with distorted face, he glared around, silently laughing in savage delight. This was easy—so far. Two of them gone, he only had three now to deal with. Three warriors fighting for their lives.

Not a sound. Then—a little flock of pigeons emerged from the tufted grasses on his left and hurried away. Nemarluk immediately started crawling to the left, noiselessly but quickly worming his way among the grass and rocks and shrubs. He located his man, despite the pipe-clay and ochre making his body almost invisible as he crouched against a yellowish-brown boulder. Nemarluk's arm let fly and his third spear shot straight into the back of the crouching warrior.

As the man screamed Nemarluk was already swiftly worming his way again to the left, for keen eyes would be searching here now. Dropping into the ravine he ran along it in the direction of the bush he had been sitting behind not twenty minutes ago. And as he ran he planted his feet where his tracks must show. He climbed out of the ravine and began worming his way back along its edge to a stunted tree from which he could peer back along the way he had come. He waited —a long time.

Then a painted man came snaking along the ravine —upon his tracks. Nemarluk's heart thumped; he grinned as a cat might grin while watching a mouse. Like a black panther the hunter came cautiously along those tracks, his eyes glaring up amongst the rocks and bushes, his ears listening. Nemarluk grinned for there was not a breath of wind, no faint current of air. Even so the hunter smelt the grease upon Nemarluk's body—but the spear was already in mid air and caught him full upon the chest. He screamed once and fell back, his chest split open.

Nemarluk crawled on to higher ground and waited. The last remaining man, hearing that scream, would come.

Two hours went by. Far up, an eagle-hawk appeared like a speck in the blue. It grew larger, then it circled and circled. It could see the two live men; knew the four dead ones were there. Presently, another eagle appeared, effortlessly circling far up there.

Shadows began to fall. There came the flight of heavy wings and a crow settled upon the dead branch of a stunted tree. Shrewdly the black bird glanced about then stared across towards Nemarluk.

And Nemarluk knew the other man must be lying near him.

"Kark!" Heavy wings again and another crow settled upon the tree. Soon, there were seven of them; then a dozen. And still they came, in twos and threes.

Presently one flapped below. Another followed him, the coast was clear. They began all dropping down except a sentinel who remained on the dead branch peering towards Nemarluk.

Yes, the coast was clear. An eagle, volplaning down, settled on a rock. The fierce bird glanced around. Presently it, too, dropped by the crows around a dead man.

The shadows lengthened. Then Nemarluk leaped up as a head rose before him. Blade clashed against blade as they snatched one another's spear wrists, swayed their glaring hate. As the avenger jerked the blade towards Nemarluk's wrist, Nemarluk twisted the wrist and leaping caught the spearshaft between his teeth. Instantly the avenger did the same, each spearshaft snapped. They sprang back only to leap forward striking with long bone daggers, and springing sideways as they struck. They crouched glaring, with every muscle, every sinew, tensely set. Two wonder athletes fighting to the death. Trained to endurance since babyhood these two picked men were human tigers of the wild. Each sprang at the other's throat while the enemy's foot shot out—to instantly dodge Nemarluk's snatching hand. He, too, then sprang and kicked. But the enemy dropped to his knees and sprang under Nemarluk's guard only to be met by a bunched knee. Again they leaped apart.

The few stunted trees near by were now lined with crows brought to the tree tops by the sounds of combat. To a heavy flapping they were joined by the eagles. The fierce birds looked impassively on. The sun went slowly down. Silhouetted in the red glow the two crouching black figures fought on. Nemarluk buried his dagger in his enemy's thigh only to feel a dagger ripping cruelly into his shoulder. Blood streamed from their chests, their backs, their limbs. It was on blood that the enemy's foot slipped—and Nemarluk's dagger plunged straight down into his throat.

L

CHAPTER XVI

THE VALLEY OF THE DEAD

NEMARLUK was very, very thirsty. He sat a while, glaring at the dying warrior. The others had been easy, but this one had given the big chief the fight of his life. That man lying there was a warrior. But soon after daylight the hawks would be eating him.

The stars were out. A big tree silhouetted against the sky was black with crows. From another tree came a heavy flapping now and again. The eagles were roosting, too.

Nemarluk stretched out, gazing up at the stars. But he must not go to sleep lest he awake at sunrise with his eyes in the belly of an eagle. He wished that water was near. He had led an imaginary patrol to this desolate place. The nearest water was twenty miles away deep in a hidden rockhole. There were no fat paper-bark trees here with their little reserves of cool water in trunk or hollow. There was no kaolin in this barren place either—no pure, soft clay with which to close his torn skin; no dwarfed trees of any use for wounds; no roots from which to make white ash that stopped blood flowing, while it cleansed. How cool that water must be deep in that hidden rockhole twenty miles away! He must reach it before dawn otherwise he might perish, for his body was crying out for water to help make up for the blood he had lost. Wearily he arose and began searching for unbroken spears.

One by one he found the dead warriors, he had their spears to choose from, too. The weapons of a vengeance party are always the best that that particular tribe possesses.

Feeling strong again from the very feel of the weapons Nemarluk set off. With slow, long strides he walked determinedly for he must not stop until he reached water. He got there just before dawn, and drank deeply. After resting he searched for long tufts of grass. This grass he rubbed to softness then daubed it on his wounds until the clotted blood stuck it. He did the job thoroughly; if he left his wounds exposed, when he woke up they would be fly-blown. He crawled away among the rocks, and slept.

When he awoke, the sun was half way down, the afternoon was cooling. He drank. Ravenously hungry, he looked about for something he expected to find. Yes, there it was; a big carpet snake coiled up on a warm, flat rock. Killing it, he lit a fire and waited for the coals to burn down.

No animals could drink from this narrow rockhole for over it the visiting wild men always dragged a flat rock, to prevent the thirsty sun "drinking" the water. But small birds could fly down, and other creatures of the wild knew it. That is why Nemarluk expected a carpet snake to have made his home near by. He lived on the birds, and now Nemarluk, for a while, was going to live on him.

He roasted the snake and ate ravenously, his eyes towards the distant Fitzmaurice Mountains. This place was only a series of mounds and of huge boulders set in a sun-baked flat. The mountains would mean shelter. He would go to the Valley of the Dead, and there recover from his wounds and wait until he learned news. His fierce eyes glowed; he was bitter at heart. Now he could trust no man. He was no longer Nemarluk the hunted, he was Nemarluk the outcast.

Tribes that had feared him for years might still fear him, but would plot against him; their bravest men by treachery would seek his life eager to claim the honour of killing Nemarluk.

He snarled, his hand stretching out towards his spears. Oh no, Nemarluk was not dead yet. He felt certain it was Wadjee the witch doctor who had set the vengeance party to dogging him, Wadjee the jealous, who had plotted for an opportunity of doing away with a dangerous favourite. All men feared Wadjee; many men had admired Nemarluk; some had loved him.

He would have liked to turn south, to the Victoria River and Deven. But the police might be there; he must first await news from Deven. He longed for An-de-mallee camp and the camp fires of his tribesmen. But the police would be there, too.

No, he would lick his wounds in the Valley of the Dead. When strong again he would return to the plains, the swamps, and the coast. And then let any touch Nemarluk who dared.

He rested, and slept near the rockhole that night, knowing none would be following him. Thus does Mother Earth help cure her wild children's wounds— wounds that often would kill a white man. She demands only primitive treatment: drink, food, and rest.

Nemarluk started off next morning walking south as if bound for the Victoria River, and making no effort to hide his tracks. He was really making for a long strip of country that now would be almost bare of grass, the surface hard and sunbaked. He was watching also for a few paper-bark trees and presently saw them several miles away. He walked then so that the reading of his tracks would infer it was not by deliberate intention that he had passed by those trees.

He picked up several long strips of the soft, paper-like bark that had peeled from the trees. He did not pull the bark, for if any were following their sharp eyes would have noticed the fresh mark on the trunk where the bark had been peeled off.

A few miles farther on the stunted bush gave way to a strip of "scalded" ground that stretched for miles. Hard, barren, red earth that appeared as if almost every vestige of vegetation had been scalded off it. From this baked earth the winds had long since blown any trace of dust and soft sand and loam, leaving almost nothing upon which an imprint could be left.

Nemarluk walked straight out upon this scorched earth then threw a strip of the soft paper-bark before him. Standing on one leg he expertly wrapped a strip loosely around the foot of the other leg. Then treated the other foot in the same way. He now stood in rough moccasins of the softest bark, upon sunbaked earth on which a heavily-shod man could hardly have left an imprint. Changing direction abruptly, he walked towards the mountains, but at an angle and still on the hard-baked earth.

Although no eye could now detect where he had put his foot Nemarluk walked very carefully, eyeing the ground ahead. Just here and there would be a loose, wind-blown twig. If Nemarluk snapped that twig it could betray him, for a tracker would pick it up and see that the twig had been freshly snapped. Even though he did not break it such a chip could still betray him; a tracker might carefully pick it up and see the faint impression made by the stick, so proving that the weight of a man had pressed it ever so faintly upon the earth. Nemarluk was also careful to avoid an occasional drooping tuft of dead grass.

If his foot should press that down it could certainly betray him to any one following. Just here and there was a little patch of gravel to which he gave a wide berth; even one solitary little pebble he would note yards away and step carefully away from it. For the foot of a man, even though softly cushioned with paper-bark, may press a pebble, or dislodge it. And when a pebble lies freshly upturned it glints its bright side to the sun.

Upon this hard-baked floor, too, would be, just every here and there, the tiniest depression perhaps the size of a dinner plate, where a soft spot of earth had been blown out of the harder ground by the winds. Into the depression left by this soft spot a few grains of wind-blown sand would have been collected and imprisoned. Should Nemarluk step here those few sand grains would be pressed down. There might not be enough grains to make an impression such as a white man would notice, but the eagle eye of a tracker would see it. And that would be enough.

Very carefully Nemarluk had swathed those moccasins around his feet for not one shred of bark must be lost. A shred of bark the size of an inch of string would betray him, for there was no paper-bark tree here.

Just one cracked twig, just one upturned pebble, just one grass blade pressed down, just a dozen grains of sand pressed together, just a commotion on an ant run—the ants removing dead bodies crushed by a human foot, just an accidental jab of his spear point into the hard earth. Just any one of these little things and a pursuing tracker would know all.

He would hurry then, miles ahead if need be, to

where the scorched earth must meet the usual country. And there on the softer country he would search for the tracks to "come out"; he would cut those tracks and thus follow on after his man.

But a thin "finger" of this country petered off into a creek. Nemarluk knew this. Within four miles the scorched earth had narrowed to a lane on each side of which grew luxuriant grass. And that lane of scorched earth carried on until it ended right under the branches of trees, fifty yards from a creek. Nemarluk leaped up, seized a branch, swung himself up, and took off the paper-bark. Carefully he wound it in his belt, not losing one betraying shred. Then walked along the branch to the tree trunk, then out along a farther branch to the branch of an adjoining tree. Thus from branch to branch, tree to tree until he was out over the shallow water. There he dropped down, scooped a hole in the sand under the water and buried the strips of paper-bark. Then he quietly regarded the wall of trees to either side of him, listening.

He had completely lost his tracks. For miles now he would walk up this creek until it branched in the ranges. He would not have left one solitary track for many miles. And while he travelled he would live well on fish, and tortoise, and water-rat.

There was no sound of man, no call of a hunting party, no distant chopping that told of someone cutting out a sugar bag or possum. And the trumpeting of brolgas away out on the plains, told that all was well there. He began to wade. Here at least he had the creek and the bush to himself. He would wade a little farther to where the water was deeper, then sit down and soak his wounds. They were throbbing. Sooner

or later along this creek he must surely find the
kaolin clay that heals wounds.

Three days later Nemarluk was toiling along the
dark ways in the Valley of the Dead. He felt safe
here. Among these boulders, these miles upon miles
of rocky bars, of crevice and gorge and precipitous
ravine no horses could possibly travel. The gamest
tracker, even Bul-bul would hardly dare track him
here, it would mean death. Walled in by great red
cliffs he glanced up at the ribbon of sky. Trees were
leaning over the cliff's edge away up there, some of

them almost toppling over. One night a heavy wind
would come and some *would* come crashing down.
On each side of him, at the bases of the cliffs, the dark
mouths of caves showed gloomily. Here and there

where the canyon walls were smooth and protected from rain by an overhanging ledge, giant figures, queerly painted, stared at him. These were the art galleries of his people. Python and crocodile, emu and wild dog; man, spearmen and women; war scenes and hunting scenes. Queer signs also that have been symbols handed down to primitive man from ages past. And queer, spidery figures that might be half-man, half-snake, or half-man and half-bird, were totem signs telling of the ancestors who had first peopled the earth. Many were the stories these queer symbols held for Nemarluk. He shivered slightly, frowning at the grotesque shadows thrown by crag and cliff. The spirits of those gone before walked here at night. But then, a hunted man sore with wounds . . . where else in perfect safety could he lie? No, he must shelter here until he was strong enough to fight again.

He walked on, alert for a wallaby. Game was scarce down here in this rocky canyon. He must seek food, and then a shelter place. He frowned at the grim mouths of the caves, he might have grim company should he enter there alone. No, he would seek shelter between two boulders, with his back to a cliff. Any possible enemy then could only approach over his feet. He would light a fire for company and sleep in that position.

His dread of the coming night, his anxiety to find a secure camping place, robbed him of his cunning in seeking game. Black night fell. He lit a fire and crawled under an overhanging boulder.

From far up the gorge came a whispering that grew into a hollow moaning with the night. Far up, he could see the rim of a cliff in starlight against a black sky. Black crags were there, and moving things that were the wind-blown branches of trees. Black monsters seemed to be leering down at him.

From far up in the skies a big wind arose.

Down through the canyon came a sighing and a shrieking. Nemarluk, crouching deep in the Valley of the Dead was alone with the spirits of the night.

CHAPTER XVII

TRAPPED

AFTER long hours, Nemarluk dozed into fitful sleep. A frightful crash, a thunderous roar striking the cliffs brought him to his feet. With beating heart he glared into blackness as thunder rolled down the canyon. Flame and a dazzling blue lit up crag and watercourse and cliff. The lightning vanished leaving Nemarluk dazzled. Then thunder crashed again, roaring down the canyon.

Nemarluk ran. And a howling wind hastened his heels.

He leaped into blackness and hurried on with trembling spears outstretched. Lightning followed him in and a skull grinned at him. Another grinned from a ledge higher up. Then blackness. Nemarluk had leaped into a burial cave of his people. On ledge after ledge their skeletons slept.

Another flash, and he stared into living eyes, the eyes of old Wadjee the witch doctor. There crouching before him was the shrivelled form of the man who had betrayed him. Nemarluk drew a long breath, slowly getting over his fright. He did not hurl a spear. He dare not attempt to kill this witch doctor while he was here about his business with the dead. Nemarluk was glad of his unseen company, crouching in the darkness opposite.

From outside came a new roaring as the storm broke in blinding rain. But the wind hurled the rain away. All night it shrieked in banshee voices moaning throughout the valley. It was a long, long night. In chill dawn Nemarluk crept out of the cave. The witch doctor had vanished.

That day nearly brought a lingering death to Nemarluk. Hungrily, his eyes searched the rock ledges, the scrub patches that here and there grew along the canyon, for sight or sign or sound of a rock wallaby. He noticed fresh tracks on a patch of drift sand and hurried eagerly forward, spear fitted to wommera. The tracks led up along the bottom of a great crevice that split one wall of the canyon. On the moist sand among the boulders fresh wallaby tracks were plain. Nemarluk's spear arm suddenly jerked back but the wallaby leaped to escape. Nemarluk ran up the dry watercourse leaping the boulders as he sought a chance for a running shot. He sprang on to a pile of drift-wood and vanished to a crackling roar of falling stones dashing against rock walls. Crashing in water among falling sticks and stones, he leaped up waving frantic arms, stumbling to his knees as a stone fell upon his head. But for that thick mop of hair his skull would have been split. He staggered up again, gasping.

The falling of debris had ceased. He saw a bright round hole up above, with far, far away a tiny circle of blue sky. He had fallen down a boil hole.

In these mountain valleys sometimes a watercourse has its boil hole. That is where, in the rainy season, the water boils over a bar to pound a hole in a patch of soft rock. In this small hole a few hard stones collect. Next season the water pounds down, the swirling stones grinding the hole deeper. Season after season the hole grows deeper and deeper, the stones in it become ground away but other heavy stones are washed in and these in turn are swirled around and around, becoming smaller and smaller as the seasons pass.

Their edges are ground away until they are as round as cannon balls. In the course of years such a boil hole may become surprisingly deep; it depends on the hardness of the rock, and whether the weight of the wet-season water still pours over the bar in exactly the same place.

Nemarluk was trapped. "Like a dingo!" he snarled.

He was in the bottom of a circular, very narrow well. But the bottom was considerably wider than higher up, for here the rock was softer and the pounding water and grinding stones of many years had cut out the bottom until this boil hole was the shape of a bottle. And Nemarluk was like an ant in the bottom of the bottle. Even he could not climb these smooth walls because of their overhanging shape. He glanced at the rubble floating around his knees. It was just a mass of rotten sticks and leaves. The storm of the night before had hardly touched this long crevice, only sufficient water had fallen down it to wash those sticks and leaves across the little round mouth of the boil hole.

Nemarluk had been badly shaken. And each deep knife wound had broken open during his frantic struggle when falling. What made him really terrified was that he was weaponless. He had dropped his spare spears up above as he crashed while the one in his hand had been smashed on the rim of the hole as he fell through. He gazed up again, a terrible longing in his face. He knew it was hopeless. The witch doctor had gone—even if he would have helped him.

Of all his many adventures, far too many to relate in this book, Nemarluk afterwards told me that being trapped alone down there was the experience which frightened him most.

Especially at night. For it was very cold and pitch

dark, just a little circle of faint light above. Sometimes he would gaze at a star like a twinkling gem of fire that seemed very close; gaze until his neck ached. Then he would sit with his knees under his chin, staring at his feet. He had made a heap of the stones and on these stacked the sodden sticks and fallen leaves. This pile reached just above the water and on it he sat. He dared not risk cramp. Although he could see nothing but death awaiting him he knew that his legs and feet must never fail him. When his neck was rested he would gaze up at the star again.

The second night he was terribly lonely, for the wail of spirits was all around him, whispering in the voices of his fathers' and of tribesmen long gone. It really was a light wind up on top.

This wind sucking down the mouth of the boil hole seemed to the superstitious captive below to be the whispering voices of the many dead.

On the morning of the fourth day he was squatting like a huge black toad. He had not quite given up hope. Something made him glance up . . . his heart ceased beating, then it went "Thump! thump! thump!"

The ugliest, the funniest, the loveliest thing was glaring down at him, a little black dwarf man in the brilliant ring of sunlight away above. Then, beside those humped shoulders, that ugly head, appeared the head of the ugliest old gin in the mountains.

To Nemarluk's burning eyes came the light of understanding, from his throat came a funny noise, the gladdest cry he had ever uttered.

"Nemarluk!" came a shriek from above.

Slowly Nemarluk stood up; he was very weak. "I'm trapped!" he called. And waited.

Both heads disappeared. There came the sound of

excited talk, the sweetest music to Nemarluk's ears. Then the two grotesque heads appeared again.

"Are you hungry?" shrilled the dwarf.

Nemarluk laughed.

"Catch!" shrilled a voice. Nemarluk held up his hands and down came the roasted leg of a wallaby. Nemarluk wolfed it as the heads disappeared.

He stood there happily, gnawing the bone as a dog would gnaw it. After a long while he grinned; they were dragging a tree along. Slowly they did it, the little dwarf man and the crippled, ugly old gin. He could hear the long sapling dragging over sand, over rocks; could now hear them gasping. That sapling would have to be very long, it would be heavy to these two small ones. The two ugly heads appeared again.

"Stand aside!" shrilled the dwarf. "Stand aside!" shrilled the gin.

Then Nemarluk saw the butt end of a long, dead sapling appear over the hole. It began to creep down as they upended it. They clung to it as well as they could but they had to tip it almost upright to allow it to come down the little hole. Then its weight took it, Nemarluk heard two gasps, then two shrieks.

"Look out!"

And down came the pole with a rush. It reached to nearly the rim of the hole.

"Wait a little!" shrieked the dwarf.

Nemarluk waited, and presently heard them coming panting back. Then down the hole trailed thick strong vines roughly twisted.

Nemarluk began to climb the pole. Only when on top did he realize how very weak he was. But his face seemed to become the face of a boy again. He laughed at them; thumped them on the back; shook them;

made much of them. And they stood there rocking
under his big hands, their funny faces twisted into
distorted grins. They gazed up as Nemarluk laughed;
laughed at them, at the cliffs, at the skies; then happily
laughed at his spears still lying where they had fallen.

Nemarluk was alive again; was a boy again.

The dwarf and the old woman stared at him in
awe. But he shook them again, and their ugly faces
crinkled into sympathetic grins. The dwarf drew himself up to his full tiny height, clutching his little spears.

"You want the feel of a fire," he said importantly;
"she will light one for you while I hunt that you may
eat."

And he strode away.

The old woman grinned fearfully, then limped away
and began gathering tinder. Nemarluk watched her
as she crouched down twirling her firestick. The big
chief's heart warmed to this poor old thing. Long ago
she had been terribly burned, she was almost shapeless.
She was the faithful companion of the little dwarf;
she looked after him and was very proud of him.

She boasted of him around the camp fires of their
tribe. He was a mighty hunter so she swore, a great
man; she defied any woman to say there was a better
man in the land. The little man loved to hear her
speak of him so, his tiny chest would swell with pride.
He would have protected her with his life, if need be.

Nemarluk knew the queer hill tribe to whom these
two people belonged. A tribe which lived just on the
edge of the plains, and just within the first barrier
of the ranges. Good hunters, these people, but a shy,
timid tribe. Still, for ages past they had proved capable
of holding their own among the craggy hills of their
tribal grounds. But they preferred to keep to themselves, always seeking to avoid the surrounding tribes.

Nemarluk spread out his limbs to the fire, although it was a warm day. Like all primitive people he loved fire. And now his limbs were stiff after those three days and nights down there in the cold hole. He laughed as he talked to the woman. She answered shyly, only glancing at him now and then from half-frightened eyes. Nemarluk the big chief was known to her people but it was rarely he had visited them.

The dwarf returned in an hour's time with a freshly speared wallaby draped around his neck. The old woman grinned her pride; she "knew he'd do it!" Nemarluk was hearty in his applause and the dwarf nearly fell over at such praise from the warrior chief.

He slung down the wallaby with a grunt and the woman immediately set about cooking it. She simply spread out the coals and threw the wallaby upon it. Nemarluk's nostrils quivered to the odour of the singed fur.

CHAPTER XVIII

THE DWARF

THAT night Nemarluk lay at ease, close by the friendly fire. His wounds were dressed with goanna oil, kaolin, and soothing ashes, for the dwarf was an expert with wounds, and prided himself on being a doctor. He was good, too.

With great care he had prepared these healing clays and ashes so as to separate the useless matter in them from the healing. He dressed Nemarluk's wounds, working silently, a frown on his stubby little face; he was as painstaking as any doctor. The old woman was his assistant.

Nemarluk lay back with a sigh. His body felt wonderfully rested, the burning was rapidly going from his wounds.

The dwarf and his old woman friend were in the Valley of the Dead searching for herbs that only grew here. He explained how he had seen Nemarluk's tracks and followed them up. He gave Nemarluk news of the police for even his tribe had been raided some time ago.

"I faced them with my spears!" shrilled the dwarf.

"Yu ai!" nodded the old woman.

"I would have killed the white policeman had he not been so quick!" boasted the dwarf.

"Yu ai!" agreed the old woman.

The little man really had been brave. Constable Langton suddenly appeared before him in the steely light of dawn. The dwarf had really leaped up and threatened with shaking spear, the old woman glaring behind him. Langton had brushed the little man aside and carried on with the raid.

"They had Chugulla on a chain," said the dwarf. "Two white police were there, and Bul-bul and Tommy the tracker and other trackers I did not know. But Tiger's men had gone two days before. They caught Tiger's wife though and she told them Tiger's Mob had killed the white men. She told them Tiger had gone to the Daly River for the ceremonies."

"The white police have caught them all now," frowned Nemarluk.

"So the smokes told us," replied the dwarf, "but you can rest in peace. The white police are far away."

They were too. Constable Langton was hurrying on the return trip back to Darwin, by Timber Creek then the Katherine, a thousand miles of trackless country. He must beat the wet season. His prisoners were Tiger's Mob, one of the toughest little bands of aboriginals that ever roamed the north. Twice they tackled him, even with steel upon their wrists they rushed him and tried to tear him to pieces. A thousand miles of anxiety and hardship in which even horses floundered and perished. But he got through.

And Tiger was caged.

The dwarf and the misshapen old woman stayed with Nemarluk three weeks. His wounds healed, quickly he became the Nemarluk of old. He admired the hunting prowess of the dwarf. The little man had the keenest eyes, the keenest hearing, the keenest scent. Nature had recompensed him for his tiny height. His little body was a ball of muscle and sinew, he could climb cliffs that the powerful Nemarluk could never have climbed; like a monkey he could work his way along a narrow ledge far up and spear the little cliff wallabies sheltering there. He could worm his way far into crevices in the rocks seeking his precious herbs, or the snake or furry little animal sheltering there; could vanish in a second upon ground on which it would seem a bird could hardly hide; could climb the tallest trees and creep out on branches that would break under the weight of an ordinary man.

Nemarluk slowly realized that this despised little creature could do things he, a noted hunter, could not do. He would never have noticed it had he not been compelled to now lead an inactive life and depend on these two strange people. Ungrudgingly he praised them; and they loved his praises. Poor creatures, they had never had any one to praise them before.

At night time the dwarf whispered fascinating stories. His eyes grew wide, he whispered very earnestly while the old woman listened and stared at Nemarluk's face. Nemarluk listened intently, never smiling, for he had heard of some of these things before.

"I am a giant!" hissed the dwarf, "a giant bigger than you, as the messmate is to the shrub. I am a terrible giant to all the tiny people. But they like me. Sometimes I meet them. They come to me, they show me things, they talk in funny ways." And he hissed, with tiny, quick little hisses, then with laughing little hisses.

"Yes," he whispered, "they laugh just like we laugh and their faces all crinkle up. They grow very angry too, then they look ugly. Some are no bigger than your finger. They have their little women too, the little women have lots of hair—as much as you have on one eyebrow."

And so the dwarf would tell them of the fairy people he met, here in the Valley of the Dead and in distant places as well. Tiny people who lived in the cracked walls of caves deep within the cliffs. Little people who came out into the sunlight or moonlight on ledges high up, to laugh and play and pop back into the cracks like a baby 'roo into the pouch of its mother.

Nemarluk, now he was strong again, grew very restless.

Far away in the lagoons the crocodiles were lying; the plains, where the huntsmen had burned the dry grass, would now be carpets of green; the turtle were stirring deep down in the now moistened mud. For the early storms had come, the wet season was almost upon them, the patrols would have vanished until after the wet. A fierce longing seized Nemarluk for An-de-mallee camp and the fires of his people. One morning the strange three passed down the Valley of the Dead and on among the foothills, the long strides of Nemarluk growing so eager that the two little people behind him had to run to keep up. They came out on to the plains to see green clouds in the distance—the trees and foliage surrounding the swamps.

The heart of Nemarluk was singing. With a boyish laugh, though regretfully, he turned to farewell the two who had been and would still prove to be faithful friends. The frowning little dwarf and the old crippled woman were nearly crying. Nemarluk would leave them now, for his home was far away towards the coast. They must turn back into the foothills where their people were already congregating in the caves that would give them shelter throughout the wet season.

"Ma-muck!" laughed Nemarluk. "Farewell! Farewell! When the rains cease I will visit you again and we will hunt together. From now on when I visit your tribe we three shall *always* hunt together. Ma-muck."

"Ma-muck!" they muttered. "Ma-muck!"

And Nemarluk strode on into the bush, laughing his hunting song. Again and again he turned to "Yak-ai!" and wave. They shouted back, and waved.

Presently, he could see them no more. But still,

growing fainter and fainter now, they heard his "Yak-ai!" coming ringing through the bush.

And he smiled as faintly their answer came "Yak-ai!" "Yak-ai!"

The early storms came in earnest. Then leaden skies, fierce winds, and rain. Alternate sunshine and rain for a while. Then steady rain. The wet season had come.

Dry ravines were creeks, creeks were rivers, rivers were raging floods. The swamps overflowed on to the plains, one large area of the Wild Lands became a small inland sea. The wild people huddled in gunyah

and cave while the bitter rains were on, to come out
with the sunlight and hunt. Then back to their caves
again, eager for the wet to be over so that they could
swarm out on to the plains and hunt.

Large areas of the land grew noisy with wet season
life. The "Quart pot! Quart pot! Quart pot!" "Croak!
Croak! Croak!" of battalions of frogs. The "Gark!
Gark! Gark!" of the wild swan. The whistling wings
from armies of arriving waterfowl, the honking and
trumpeting of geese, the whistling of ducks, the hoarse
cackling of the night heron. The moon came peeping
out from black clouds and her face was fanned by
wings as wild geese honked by. Out on the plains was
a flapping and a trumpeting and a loud "Goork!
Goork! Goork!" "Gah! Gah! Gah!" as native companions played and danced. A thousand different bird-
calls rang out all over the land, happy calls for the good
earth was come to fresh life again. Some wild things
that had burrowed deep to sleep throughout the wet
now came gladly to the surface to greet a new season.

After the rains Nemarluk was happy again for these
last four months had been secure from the ceaseless
pursuit. With his own people around him, he was a
king again. Alas, he had found no warriors who could
take the place of his Red Band. But he was wild and
free and among his own people, and now the wet
season was over. All the earth, all living things were
bursting with new life under a glorious sun. Nemarluk
led his people towards the Moyle.

And behind them there followed two warriors. Grim
men, brave men, for night and day at every moment
they carried their lives in their hands. Far from friends
they were completely encompassed by enemies. Dis-
covery meant certain death.

No wonder they were ceaselessly alert, their every movement cautious, prepared for instant action night and day. The flight of a bird, the rustle of a snake in the grass, the thud of a wallaby disturbed in the undergrowth—all held a double meaning for them. The howl of a dingo in the night, the hoot of an owl, the screech of a night hawk might be neither wild dog nor bird. A broken bush, a torn shred of bark, a track that told of a running man or the dawdling footprints of women and children each told a tale of security or danger. The distant sound of a rude axe chopping a tree for sugar-bag or log for bandicoot, a hunting call floating over plain or swamp all held their meaning. The corroboree song from a camp at night, or sudden silence, all held a meaning for these hunters of men. Any sign or sound or movement could mean that they were still safe, or that their enemies were suspicious, or that they were discovered.

As they walked cautiously on they were continually reading the ground before them, the country ahead to right and left and behind, their ears keyed to receive the slightest sound. As they turned questioning heads not only were they seeing and listening, they were also smelling, smelling for the smoke of some hidden little fire where truant gins might be squatting around a roasted possum, smelling for the taint of a grease-covered tribesman who might be indulging in forty winks, watching carefully lest some ambitious picca-ninny might have strayed behind to chase a lizard. Let these two hunters stumble upon stragglers, let but their tracks be seen, and they instantly would be the hunted with a hundred men upon their trail.

Away out over the plain came a wild, piercing cry. The hunting call of Nemarluk.

The hunters stood stock-still; then looked at one another, grinning meaningly. Very cautiously they stepped forward.

For weeks now they had been trailing Nemarluk. But Nemarluk had never left his own people; the warriors of his tribe had always been with him. Except at night. When it grew very dark he had crept away, vanished into the night and always slept alone.

And they had never been able to find him. For even an aboriginal, unless in moonlight on soft country, cannot see tracks at night.

On moonlight nights Nemarluk left no tracks, for he disappeared into the blackness of vine jungle or mangrove.

These two hunters for weeks had been trying to catch Nemarluk alone and sleeping away from his tribesmen. They had crept night after night within sight of his camp fires, but had never seen him vanish. Nor located him afterwards.

As well as being a matter of life and death, it was an extraordinarily difficult task these hunters had set themselves to do. To track Nemarluk, even when he was alone in the bush, was like tracking a lion to its lair. But these two hunters also had to unerringly judge day by day, night by night, which way the tribe was travelling—or hunting. For they must keep in that direction from the tribe in which it would be almost certain no people would return. If they were in the wrong position the tracks of the hunters would be seen. Often while the tribe was camped for days the two hunters were forced to hide a long way away. For the tribesmen and women day by day would go in all directions from the camp, and return from all directions.

Although the aboriginal can travel over any country,

he naturally prefers to walk over the easiest ground and thus save his feet. Thorn and rock and mud he avoids when possible. This fact sometimes gave the hunters the chance to spy a camp at night; they would creep over the bad ground which occasionally hedged a camp.

When the tribesmen were camped right on the coast it was easier, for the two hunters would wade along the shore and come up behind the camp with the tide. Now they were following in the tracks of Nemarluk's tribe as the Cahn-mah happily hunted their way towards the great swamps, and Meewa plain, and the Big Ring Corroboree camps. There was little chance now of any of these people doubling back and finding the avengers' tracks. But when the Cahn-mah joined in the Meeting of the Tribes there would be four hundred able-bodied warriors, all excited at the approaching ceremonies.

Then let the hunters beware should they be discovered. Two big men these; powerful, brainy, and certainly brave. Both were heavily cicatrized across shoulders and chest, the marks of full warriors. Each wore a human hair belt, and had a bone dagger stuck in the thick hair just above the ear; was marked in ochre with his totem markings, wore arm bands and head bands and feathers. And each had wommera and heavy spears carried slung to a native belt in such a way that they would not click. One man was more heavily built than the other, with a broad, intelligent face from which gleamed deep-set, savage eyes. The eyes of the other held a cold stare, his leaner face impassive and expressionless. A human bloodhound this one, but the other had the better brain.

Their courage particularly impressed me. In the weeks and the months to come these men almost certainly would be discovered and then if caught their kidney fat would be hacked out while they were still alive; they would live to see it fought for and rubbed on the bodies of the victors.

But they pressed on.

For Nemarluk the next month sped by in the excitement of the Big Corroborees. He was easy in his mind about the police for Deven had sent him word that the patrols were seeking him in the Victoria River country. Nemarluk laughed boisterously. When the patrols got tired and sought him in this direction, he would make for the Victoria. Meanwhile, he was safe.

But he was not safe.

One dreamy afternoon he was wading for turtle in a lily lagoon; a beautiful sheet of water hedged by white paper-barks and covered with enormous lily leaves. So large are some of these leaves that a baby piccaninny can be seated upon one and it will not sink. Among these leaves and tall water plants many young ducks were hiding from the waders. Nemarluk was stirring up the bottom with his feet, feeling for tortoise. He was almost alone, for his tribesmen were wading at the distant end of the lagoon. Nemarluk thought he touched a tortoise and swiftly reached down as his ankles were suddenly gripped and he was tugged under. Utter surprise unnerved him until fingers clutched for his throat. He doubled up and plunged to the surface with a splash and snort like a hippopotamus to howl aloud to his tribesmen, who saw him plunging towards them, hoarsely shouting. Before long all were excitedly talking around the mysterious spot.

But there was nothing to see—just the stirred up

water and wisps of floating weed disturbed in the struggle. The tribesmen gazed towards the shore, anxious because of enemies they could not understand. Nemarluk declared it was a man's hand that had clutched for his throat, and it must have been a man's hand that had snatched his ankles. He had not stepped on a crocodile, or slipped on a slimy log.

They separated and waded to the edge of the lagoon, but could find no tracks.

They whispered together, clutching spears and staring about anxiously. Nemarluk felt sure it was Wadjee the witch doctor who had set enemies upon him. At Wadjee's name, all shivered. No man there wished to be at enmity with the dreaded witch doctor. To search for the tracks of his agents might well mean death to the man who found them.

"Again I am a hunted man," hissed Nemarluk, "and a man without friends. I've lost my Red Band; Tiger's Mob is gone. The jealousy of Wadjee sees its chance. By treachery he will get rid of me—if he can."

All returned to the big camp, very uneasy, suspicious and frightened. And the first man Nemarluk saw there was the withered old witch doctor. They glared into one another's eyes. Long ago, at the height of his popularity, Nemarluk would instantly have accused this snake in the grass. Now he dared not. The dreaded witch doctor had many friends, friends so afraid of him that they would fight to win his favour.

That night Nemarluk was very careful where he slept.

CHAPTER XIX

PHANTOM PURSUERS

A WEEK later Nemarluk again almost met tragedy although he did not know it until long afterwards. While hunting in forest country he spied a sugar-bag in the branch of a tall tree. In a moment he was climbing the tree and soon his tomahawk was ringing through the bush as he cut out the wild bees' nest. A startled wallaby hopped from cover, sat back on its tail, then seeing some tribesmen grouped around the tree, bounded away. With a loud "Yak-ai!" the tribesmen raced in pursuit cheered on by Nemarluk above. Then he was alone, his tomahawk blows ringing out sharp and clear.

Two hunters crept from cover and, crouching low, hurried towards the tree. Their eyes held an eager grin, they breathed deeply from suppressed excitement. At last!

Nemarluk opened the nest and regardless of the angry bees reached in his hand for the honeycomb—the aboriginals' greatest natural luxury. He ate half, then with the rest began climbing down the tree.

The hunters crept nearer.

From among the trees a solemn-faced piccaninny appeared, big-eyed with anticipation. How he loved honey! He toddled closer, gazing up at Nemarluk coming down the tree. He would just stand there and perhaps the big chief would give him a fistful of sugar-bag. He felt sure he would.

And the big chief did, with a laugh. The two hunters crouching close by ground their teeth in rage as an anxious mother appeared, calling for her child. A young lubra, she came shyly, smiling as she saw the big chief. In the distance came the shouts of the warriors, returning with the wallaby.

The two hunters crept away.

Soon afterwards Nemarluk left the Big Ring camp abruptly, with all his people. It happened this way. It was the end of the third big corroboree night, and nearly dawn. Worn out with excitement and dancing Nemarluk glided away to sleep. His sleeping place was always some distance away and he never slept in the same place twice. But to-night, well to-night was almost done, and last night's camping place was very comfortable and very safe. It was deep within a thicket of pandanus palms. The long, dry leaves were piled thick upon the ground and anything approaching in the night would cause a noise, crackling. Nemarluk could get to his sleeping place quietly by stepping from log to log, but any one not knowing the place could not possibly hope to do so in the night. Nemarluk, heavy-eyed, almost asleep on his legs, decided he would sleep there again this night.

The night was dark, the palm thicket inky black, Nemarluk was invisible as his sensitive feet felt their way deep into the thicket. Upon a couch of grass he sank to rest—and hands closed upon him. With a startled yell he heaved up and crashed rolling into the darkness as clutching hands snatched at him.

As well try to hold a buffalo bull. Nemarluk bolted and the noise he made would have put a buffalo to shame.

Brought to a halt by the palm trunks the hunters panted there in maddened wrath. So sure were they of Nemarluk that they had not waited for him to fall asleep. They had made just that one vital mistake.

Nemarluk was mad with himself. Never again would he sleep in the same place twice. An hour later, Nemarluk, with the Cahn-mah at his heels, was silently leaving the sleeping camp. They travelled fast. In Nemarluk's footsteps there stepped in turn half the tribe, blotting out his tracks.

Back at Indee and An-de-mallee camp and the coast, Nemarluk with his tribesmen felt safe from the intrigues of the witch doctor. He was certain the jealous old plotter had set killers upon his tracks, totembrothers probably of that five who had never returned. But these new killers would hardly dare pursue him here. They would wait their chance until the tribe resumed their nomadic life, until some day when Nemarluk strayed from camp or hunting party.

"What I have done to five," thought Nemarluk grimly, "I'll do to these others also—when the time comes."

Meanwhile he planned to enjoy a joke at the expense of the white police. So he led his people on walkabout up along the coast to the Daly River. Here, they gazed out on the broad river with its crocodiles sunning themselves on the muddy banks. There was good fishing here in river and sea, and on the level country were plentiful yams for the women to dig.

Nemarluk kept to the Lower Daly. There were no white men here, the little settlement and police station were miles higher up river.

To smoke signals men of the Mulluk-Mulluk and Brinken and Dilik-Dilik came visiting with the news. The Daly River policeman with his trackers, so they said, was still at the police camp; there was no sign of movement on this edge of the Wild Lands.

Nemarluk grinned as he pictured the white police

searching for him along the distant Victoria. When they tired of the search there and returned inland he would take to the coast, slip past them and go on to the Victoria.

Happy days passed as they hunted the wide river mouth by foot and canoe.

Then there came a night when Nemarluk could not sleep. He felt terribly uneasy, he could not understand why. He was in a secure place, in pitch blackness in a tangle of vine and scrub a considerable distance from his sleeping people. But he could not sleep. Some deep, primitive instinct was warning him of danger.

Next morning he took his people straight back to An-de-mallee camp. With long strides he led the way, a frown upon his brow, his favourite dog at his heels. After a few days at An-de-mallee, he led the horde into the sand-dunes and they roamed for days hunting and fishing along the fringe of the coast.

Then there came another night when Nemarluk could not sleep. To his straining ears it seemed the spirits of his fathers were urgently whispering to him.

He was crouched beside a bar of rock covered with creepers and trailing vines. Here grew that coastal jungle which hedges many a salt-water creek along this coast. His rocky mound was perched above the creek bank, crocodiles could not crawl to him in among these vine-entangled rocks. Neither could enemies creep upon him from behind unless they braved the terrors of the crocodile-infested creek in black night. Even so the splash would betray them for they would speed desperately across that creek. The creek however offered a getaway to Nemarluk. If instant danger threatened he would leap into the creek and chance it.

But there appeared no sign of danger. And yet he could not sleep. Something was warning him.

N

Inch by inch he began to leave the shelter of the rocks, to crawl back to the creek edge and then along the high bank. There was a deathly silence, a pitch blackness in which fire-flies glowed. Then he heard a furious splash from unseen water, hoarse angry grunts. The crocodiles were fighting; pity help any living thing that fell down there. Slowly Nemarluk crawled along the edge of the bank. He paused, listening for any sound from his sleeping place. There was none; but he felt sure something was crawling there.

He crept farther and farther away.

Next morning he left the tribe, determined to "lose himself" from these invisible pursuers. He took to the sea edge, allowing the tide to wash out his tracks. Across the mud flats he found plentiful shell-fish as he walked along, and fish in the shallows upon the sandy beaches.

Beside him the shore was densely hedged with mangroves; to his right was the blue sea, a canoe like a dot bobbing upon the horizon. He walked leisurely, knowing he was losing his tracks and that no one could follow him now.

But they *were* following—within the mangroves a mile behind. Now and again a savage face would peer at the big warrior walking the beach away ahead. Then the two hunters would hurry on through the mangroves, a tiring job amongst those countless roots. Again and again they were forced to cross a salt-water creek, choosing the shallows where possible. Any crocodile lurking there they could see.

At sundown Nemarluk cooked his fish on a sheltered part of the beach where the incoming tide would wash all traces of the fire away. After dark he waded with the tide up a shallow inlet hedged with jungle. He climbed the roots up on to the bank and stepped on a carpet of leaves six inches deep. On these leaves he would leave no tracks. He walked deep into the jungle, lay down a while, then crawled farther away to sleep.

And the hunters in the night could not locate him. They crawled through the jungle; smelt the still moist air; listened for any incautious cough or yawn or snore, for any faint sound of a sleeping body rolling upon spear hafts. But they found no trace of the sleeping man.

At daylight Nemarluk was again wading the beach. Throughout the days that followed he lazed along, alone with the sea and the breeze, the forest and mangrove, and the maze of salt arms of the sea.

One morning he lay in a jungle nest until long after daylight. Lazily he arose, picked up his spears, and noiselessly started towards the creek. Suddenly he crouched down, staring at the mast of a ship. The top of the mast was just visible in the sky space amongst the trees.

He listened. There came the sound of voices deadened by undergrowth, the creak of rowlocks as a dinghy was rowed down the creek. . . . A pearling lugger had ventured into the creek seeking fresh water and wood.

Like a black panther he crept forward until from the vines he stared down on the lugger. Four Japanese were on deck and eight aboriginal crew boys. They were all well armed, the crew boys nervously watching the banks. They must have been in desperate need of water to take such a risk. They were. The lugger could have cruised outside but the crew had refused to row ashore. So Captain Arita had been forced to take the lugger into the creek. The captain felt relieved in mind as he watched the dinghy pulling down the

creek to the lugger, loaded with tins of fresh water.
A few more trips and they would fill the ship's tank.
Quickly then they'd sail from this lonesome spot,
notorious haunt of wild men.

Two Japanese with rifles ready sat in the dinghy,
an aboriginal seaman was at the oars, four more
crouched in the dinghy gazing anxiously at the dense
wall of trees on either side.

Captain Arita stood by the mainmast. He leaped aside
as a spear grazed his neck and buried itself quivering
in the mast. All hands instantly crouched behind the
cabin top and the Japanese began firing wildly towards
the trees. The dinghy seemed to leap through the
water.

Nemarluk sneered his rage, to think he should have
missed a grown man standing within nice range! But
it had been a very difficult shot to aim the long spear
among the trees and creepers. He crouched there glaring, hoping for another chance.

Brown Jap men of long ago had caused him all his
present trouble. These men were invaders of his land,
Nemarluk's country. He snarled as the dinghy dashed
along the opposite side of the lugger, and crouching
men lifted the water tins aboard. Then Captain Arita
shouted an order, soon then the dinghy sped as if
pulling to the opposite shore. She was towing the
lugger. And how the crew bent to the oars, the dinghy
out of spearshot from Nemarluk but within easy throw
of the opposite bank. The lugger began to creep ahead.

Captain Arita shouted an order but the crew boys
point blank refused. A Japanese sprang up the mast,
keeping it between him and Nemarluk's bank. This
look out man tried to peer back among the trees while
keeping a look out for canoes to appear racing across

the creek mouth. They expected the jungle to fill with howling savages.

But the only noise was from the straining oars and the hoarse call of cranes disturbed by the gunshots.

Nemarluk began creeping along the bank, hoping for a shot. Suddenly, the look out man shouted, and pointed. To Nemarluk's surprise the man seemed to be pointing behind him. Renewed shots broke out. Then Nemarluk froze to the earth. He had not been seen, but the look out man had seen—something behind him. Nemarluk leaped up and raced like a cassowary up the creek, dodging tree trunks and vines; almost with the speed of the great bird, he sped on.

CHAPTER XX

A FRIEND IN NEED

NEMARLUK had instantly made up his mind. By careful walking he could leave no tracks on this soft carpet of leaves, for these were jungle leaves, very different to the sun-dried, brittle leaves of the open forest. But it was useless delaying to hide tracks for his pursuers could hasten to the open forest country, circle the jungle creek and cut his tracks where he came out of the jungle. There would be only one puzzle for them to solve. He might cross the creek then hurry down the jungle on the bank opposite and emerge on the seashore, then resume his wadings down the coast again. Or he might run the creek to its head and make his escape inland. The puzzle was for them to solve.

Nemarluk had instantly decided to strike straight inland to the mountains. Again and again he had outwitted the police patrols by doubling back and making for the country they had just left. He could outwit these native enemies similarly, by making straight for the witch doctor's country.

He was positive it was Wadjee's men who were dogging him.

Within a few miles he came to the edge of the scrub country; sunlight was bright beyond. He peered across at the open country. Spread out there directly in front were flocks of native companions, their long necks and heads high above the grass. To the watcher there came trumpet call after trumpet call as the graceful birds played and danced. With big wings outspread running swiftly forward to jump in great hops then leap around

and dance, bird after bird was dancing and playing
and trumpeting.

There could be no danger near, no unusual thing
prowling about, nothing that the birds knew of, anyway. Nemarluk stepped out from cover and strode on.
On this open country he made all speed, his eyes roving
to right and left and ahead, and to the ground. He
cut no tracks, saw no agitated or curious move of bird
or animal. That meant the men had doubled back to
the coast anticipating that he would wade the beach.
Or it could mean that he had been speedier than they.
Thinking quickly as he hurried on he pictured his
enemies dashing back to the beach. It would take them
hours to make sure he had not come out there. Then
they must follow up the salt-water creek to the forest
and circle to find where he had come out of the
jungle. He grinned. If they had hurried to the beach
then it would mean they could not cut his tracks by
nightfall. He would have gained a start which they
could never overtake.

In anger and disdain Nemarluk hurried on, keeping
clear of clumps of trees, of scrub patches and grassy
hollows, of sand mounds and gullies where men ahead
might lie in ambush. He had grown very cautious
these last two years. No longer was he King of the
Wilds who put his foot wherever he willed. He had
learned that only by ceaselessly using his wits could
he hope to outwit his enemies.

A black-soil plain tufted with buffalo grass appeared
ahead. Nemarluk kept straight on; a plan was forming
in his mind. Chugulla's and Tiger's country lay up
along the higher Fitzmaurice near the witch doctor's
country. He would seek Tiger's tribesmen; collect the
best he could among them, then double back on his
tracks and exterminate these mysterious killers. He

must exterminate them. He frowned, glancing around. The white police sought him; a vengeance band had sought him; these mysterious ones now sought him. He must wipe them out and their fate would terrorize the others. Otherwise he was done. He might hold his freedom against the police patrols, but if every dingo in the land now felt free to hunt him, he must go down sooner or later. Grinding his teeth in rage, he rattled his spears and hurried on.

He crossed the plains and pushed on into the country of the swamps. Now and then he cut the tracks of a hunting party; sometimes he saw a smoke that was signal or hunting fire but he avoided all. He was suspicious of every living thing now.

In a few days Nemarluk was in among the foothills, travelling cautiously. He did not know where the police patrols might be. Bitterly he realized that, now the Red Band and Tiger's Mob were gone, Nemarluk roamed alone and the watchers on the isolated look outs hardly cared whether they signalled a patrol or not. He was friendless. Cautiously he pressed on. He must go through the witch doctor's country to reach Chugulla's tribe. If he happened to run into a hunting band of Wadjee's men they would mob him on the instant.

A few miles behind him, two quaint people were hunting. A great warrior, although so tiny he was only an ugly little dwarf. Hobbling along behind him carrying his spare spears was surely the ugliest old gin in all the Wild Lands. Her bent, crippled old legs stepped softly in the footsteps of the dwarf warrior before her. He crept forward, his fierce little eyes roaming the grassy thickets for sight or sound of a wallaby. Suddenly he halted, staring down. The gin stopped instantly. They might have been statues these two, grotesque black statues amongst gnarled trees. But both were fierce with life.

The dwarf drew a deep breath, hissed, glared around with blazing eyes. The gin was beside him instantly. They stared at the tracks.

"Nemarluk!" hissed the dwarf. "Bul-bul!"

They stared down at this story of the wild that told them all. The tracks of their hero Nemarluk and dogging those tracks were Bul-bul the hated tracker, and another. Both sets of tracks were very fresh, the hunters were close behind the hunted man.

The dwarf's eyes were blazing as he handed all his spears except two to the gin. Then he was speeding along the tracks.

For all his tiny legs it is doubtful if any man for a short distance could run as fast, as softly as the dwarf. It is doubtful whether any man has eyes as keen, hearing as acute.

Soon the old gin was left far behind. She feared to guess what her hero would do. He, the tiny man, fast on the tracks of the giant Bul-bul, that tracker so feared throughout all the Wild Lands. With terror in her heart at the fate of the little man, she hobbled on.

Presently the dwarf passed Bul-bul and Splinter, sped around them through the bush and was running with the tracks of Nemarluk. That warrior wheeled around to a hiss, spear quivering in his hand. Wide-eyed, he stared at the panting dwarf.

"Bul-bul!" hissed the dwarf, and pointed back.

Nemarluk glanced back once and then was away like the wind. Bul-bul and the patrol right at his heels! With the speed of a deer he was racing through the bush.

The dwarf glanced after him, hesitating. Slowly, his crinkled forehead grew a hundred creases in a mighty frown, his ugly little mouth grew tight set. His spear hand clenched upon his spear, his teeth made gritting noises, his eyes shone with the vicious glare of a snake. Then crouching, he turned and ran swiftly back along his tracks.

To gain time for his friend he was going to spear Bul-bul!

He just did not have time. He got almost back to where his tracks had joined Nemarluk's. Around a clump of pandanus palms he saw Bul-bul and Splinter coming; saw Bul-bul stop and point to the dwarf's track. As Splinter came forward to stare, the dwarf's brave little spear arm swept back. He poised a second then threw just as Bul-bul glanced up. The spear hissed by Bul-bul's ear and both trackers vanished.

The dwarf fled.

Nemarluk sped straight on, past the foothills, deep into the mountains and at last in the Valley of the Dead. Horses could not come here. In this rocky fastness he turned at bay. He would await the policeman and trackers to come on foot.

But they did not come. Days passed, and still they did not come.

Nemarluk's mind was in a maze. When the dwarf hissed "Bul-bul!" he had thought a whole patrol was at his heels. Not so. It was only the two silent hunters who had hunted him day and night week after week. They were not the witch doctor's men at all, the bones of those men had long since been cleaned up by the eagle-hawks, the crows and the dingoes.

Nemarluk, hiding in the furthermost gorges did not know what to think. He felt he was cut off from every friend, from any who would give him news. Anxiously he wondered where the police patrols were. Were they waiting for him to come out of the mountains? Were they still at the Victoria? Were they at the Daly? At An-de-mallee camp? At Meewa swamp? Or away out on the plains? Or down by the coast? . . . Where were they?

To find that Bul-bul was actually on his track when he believed him hundreds of miles away had been a terrible shock.

One morning he climbed to the plateau and walked across the wind-swept summit to the edge. On a jutting ledge of rock he stood gazing out over the country below.

Below him swept the valley of the Fitzmaurice, many miles wide and hedged by red walls of cliffs as it meandered towards the plains and the sea. From the great crevices in the cliffs waterfalls sprayed down from the uplands. Far across the great valley dark green patches were scrub lands surrounded by the sunlit forest. Around all was the blue-green of the Australian bush divided by the silver streaks of waterways. Far over the valley in heavy flight black cockatoos went hoarsely screeching. Nemarluk's heart swelled proudly as he gazed over this, his native land.

Far away, like a line of little dogs there emerged the horses and mules of a patrol. Nemarluk gasped. Here! Even here. He watched them as they slowly rode across the valley, visible only occasionally as they appeared from out of a clump of timber on to some clear, grassy pocket, then vanished down a creek or on to the other side of a rise, or into timber again. Finally, they disappered.

With his back to a boulder upon which eagles had perched, Nemarluk sat for a long time, thinking. Trying to put his mind into the white man's mind, to realize just what the patrols were doing. He had lived his life and escaped for many, many moons now since the killing of the Jap men. Escaped by losing his tracks again and again, by disappearing to the sea or far back in the ranges, or by dodging back to the country from which the patrols had just ridden away. But now, things had changed. How Bul-bul came to be so close upon his tracks he could not imagine. He had shaken him off for the time being. And now, far away below him was a white patrol riding towards the Victoria River.

A sudden though struck Nemarluk. He leaped up. Instead of waiting for the patrol to leave the river he would follow in its tracks. When they entered the big area of the river lands he would be there with them, instead of far away.

Laughing as he had not laughed for weeks past he climbed down into the valley. A few hours later he was walking easily along in the very tracks of the patrol. And laughter was in his heart.

What Nemarluk did not know, but had very, very nearly guessed, was the mentality of the white men.

Constable Fitzer in charge of the little Timber Creek Police Station well knew the almost impossibility of capturing Nemarluk. This wild man was a real King of the Wilds, hunted in his own Wild Lands. He could laugh at any patrol encumbered with horses and, in some cases, frightened trackers.

But there was one man who was not frightened—Bul-bul. And Bul-bul was a power in this land, he had friends scattered far and wide.

For a long time Constable Fitzer had been working to drive Nemarluk sooner or later into some trap set by the famous tracker. Bul-bul and Splinter went back to the wilds as warriors, travelling far from the patrol. As Fitzer travelled, his main object was to keep Nemarluk ever on the move and finally drive him into the arm of Bul-bul. Long ago he had explained to Bul-bul all the moves he would make under any foreseen circumstances. Bul-bul with Splinter was to react to those moves, although working, at times far distant from the patrol, on their own.

And so, long ago, Bul-bul and Splinter had disappeared into the bush. Brave men. Bul-bul always had it in mind that, if he could not capture Nemarluk in his own lands, sooner or later he would capture him in the Victoria River country. For Nemarluk would be driven to seek companionship there with Deven and Deven's men, with his own sense of security there, and to satisfy his craving for white man's tobacco. Sooner or later, Bul-bul argued to Splinter, Nemarluk would return to the Victoria. And on the Victoria were friends of Bul-bul who would quietly let him know.

Splinter nodded, saying little. Splinter was always a silent man.

o

CHAPTER XXI

SWEET LIBERTY

DAY by day Nemarluk followed on the tracks of the patrol, a few miles behind. He became intensely interested; grinned now and then at the thought that he was really hunting himself. The thought gave him considerable pleasure. Those men riding ahead were seeking Nemarluk far and wide. Where was Nemarluk? Nemarluk grinned. He knew every move of those men ahead, the plans of the policeman, the hopes of the trackers in trying to run Nemarluk to earth. He read all this in the tracks. Within twenty-four hours he knew the tracks of every horse and mule; knew the two that were lagging behind, because the men had been forced to stop and lighten the loads of the lame animals. In future he would always recognize the dismounted tracks of the policeman and the trackers. There were one policeman and four trackers—providing no others had temporarily left the patrol before he joined the tracks.

But Bul-bul's and Splinter's tracks were not among them. Nemarluk gazed anxiously around. What if they were coming behind, tracking him? To make sure he waited a whole day up on a rocky knoll, gazing back along his tracks. But no one came. Next day by midday he had caught up with the patrol.

Sometimes the tracks of two horses would branch away from the patrol. Nemarluk would follow their tracks until he felt certain of where they were heading: to a lagoon where tribesmen might be expected to be hunting turtle or women gathering lily bulbs; perhaps to a shady creek where a deep waterhole would be a favourite fishing ground; or to climb some rocky look out. Nemarluk would know from the direction. He would then return to the tracks of the patrol, knowing that even if the two scouts caught any hunting party they would gain no information for Nemarluk had completely lost himself. He was suspicious now of all men. Certainly only he knew that Nemarluk was travelling with the patrol.

Occasionally the patrol would hide and rest by day in the heart of densely wooded country. Nemarluk would rest too, like a dozing kangaroo deep in the shade of a thicket. Just after sundown he would creep nearer the patrol. Yes, the horses were being quietly saddled up, the bell tongues tied, the pack animals carefully packed so that there could be no jingle of chain or quart pot. Then the patrol would start off out into the open country to move swiftly and keep moving throughout the night.

At dawn they would raid a native camp. Nemarluk would listen to the startled yells, the snarl of dogs, the alarmed shouts of warriors. He would growl deep down in his throat while his eyes flashed as he gripped his spears, then laugh silently.

He would picture the disappointed policeman, the sullen trackers, the weary preparations for breakfast after a hard night's ride with disappointment at the end of it.

Once, in a grassy camp encircled by dense timber, the horses and mules were left for several days in charge of two trackers, while the policeman and the other two trackers crept away in the night to surprise a wary tribe camped in a gorge fifty miles away.

By day and by night Nemarluk watched the patrol

camp from the timber, his spear arm twitching. How
he wished he had his Red Band! They would have
crept on these two trackers in the night and speared
them at dawn then raided the camp. They would have
kept the horses quiet and made an ambush for the
policeman and his two trackers when they returned.
Not a man would have escaped.

Nemarluk sighed. His Red Band was far away
behind the big walls of Fanny Bay Jail.

Could he do the job himself? He drew a long breath.
Before him, the horses and mules were quietly feeding
within a grassy pocket through which ran a stream,
green with rushes. Like a dark green circle fencing all
in, was a wall of trees dense with vine and creeper. The
camp was in the centre, packsaddles and saddles and
swags neatly piled in place. Sitting by the fire were
the two trackers, rifles handy. Very suspicious men,
frightened enough to fire at the least suspicious sound.
The camp and these men were nicely placed out of
spear-throw from the timber.

At dark those two would crawl away from the camp,
and keep very quiet. They would take some finding.
But he could find them—and spear one. But the other!
Would he use that rifle swiftly and surely, or vanish
and hurry to warn the policeman?

Nemarluk wondered. But a constantly hunted man
learns a lot. Where were Bul-bul and Splinter? Again,
there might be another patrol working with this one
a hundred miles away, and at any moment men scout-
ing from it might ride or walk into the camp. To cap
all, Nemarluk felt he had no friends, no one to flee to,
no one to back him up. If he attacked this patrol and
failed to wipe out every man, the hue and cry raised
would put him in a worse plight than ever. His only

friend was Deven. But Deven was away in the Victoria River country, on that side of the river which was not Nemarluk's country. Besides, Deven's men were not Nemarluk's men. No, he would love to attack this patrol now that it had separated, but the risk was far too great.

Nemarluk snarled, thinking deeply. The best thing to do was to keep "lost" until he and Deven could raise a band of Deven's men, the best left from Tiger's men, and the best left from his own. And then—they could do things.

The weeks went by. Eventually the patrol was forced back to Timber Creek for food. Outfitted once again, the patrol crossed the river and rode down the hundred and more miles along the other side.

Now Nemarluk had to be very careful. He was in the white man's station country, where many strange black boys were employed as stockmen. And some of these men knew his tracks, would recognize them if they saw them.

He made straight for the ranges and walked down beside them, parallel with the patrol. Thus there would be far less chance of wandering stockboys cutting his tracks.

Nemarluk and Deven met gladly. On the eyrie in the night by the glow of the fire they laughed and talked, Nemarluk in delight at the company of a friend.

"It was a cunning move," grinned Deven, "following the tracks of the police."

"I hunted myself," laughed Nemarluk, "and learned how they do it. They'll find it all the harder now to catch me. . . . But not once did I see the tracks of Bul-bul." He frowned, and Deven answered his frown.

"I can't find out where he is," he growled, "but I feel he's not far away."

"Collect your men!" suggested Nemarluk eagerly. "You have good ones. Cross the river with me now straight to Chugulla's country. Chugulla's tribe is a big tribe with some of the fiercest fighting men in the Wild Lands. Tiger's Mob were of the very best, but they were not all the good men. I'll collect a band of Chugulla's men; they'll follow me. Then, with you and your men, we'll go straight to the coast and An-de-mallee. I'll pick a band from my own Cahn-mah—form another Red Band. All together, we'll be the biggest and strongest band of fighting men who ever roamed the Wild Lands. While we stick together no patrols can ever hope to catch us."

Deven frowned. "You know why I can't cross the river into Chugulla's country," he growled: "The mountains this side of the river are my country. I and my men run this country, Chugulla's men run the Fitzmaurice; the Cahn-mah run your country towards the coast. And there are all the tribes in between. Since the white men came the gamest among all the tribes have been crossing one another's country to barter for iron and tobacco with the station boys. But no tribe has yet left the security of its own country to join with another tribe in another country."

"My Red Band and I have roamed everywhere," declared Nemarluk, proudly—"from the Daly right to the Victoria. We have crossed the Fitzmaurice when we came and went; right across the Wild Lands we have hunted and travelled and fought."

"Yes," agreed Deven. "But only you and your Red Band. The Cahn-mah has always stayed in its own country. And—you have always gone back."

Nemarluk frowned.

"I have spoken often to my own men," went on Deven, "since you've been away. The best are nearly ready to follow me. But only if you get Chugulla's men and your own men together. You will find that difficult, now that Chugulla has been taken by the white police. Wait here and see what the patrol does. Meanwhile we will plan, and talk to my men. Then you return to the Cahn-mah. Pick your men. Go then to Chugulla's country; pick another band from the best of Chugulla's men; then return all together here to my country. You will have with you a great band that will impress my men as no talk ever will. Such a band will make sure of my own home country. None dare ever betray such a strong band, and we will always be able to return here to safety when we want to. But first you must bring those warriors here. All together we will cross the river and spear all the cattle we want to. When the patrols come we will go straight out into the Wild Lands. Before the police find out how strong we are we will ambush a patrol. Then we all will be in it, every man will know all must stick together. Let us once wipe out a patrol and all the Wild Lands will join us. Then we can plan to drive the whites away altogether."

Nemarluk's eyes sparkled. Squatting there by the fire he clasped his knees and gazed out over the cliffs. The sky was blue and wonderful, nothing could hem *it* in. Golden stars up there twinkled to him stories the Old Men of the tribe had told around many a council fire. Those stars were friends from babyhood, Nemarluk knew many by name—at least his totem stars knew him. Away below were the plains and the great dark line of trees through which the broad river gleamed. Far out beyond the river stretched the plain far away to the Cahn-mah and the Daly.

Nemarluk breathed deeply. Everything was so big, so free, he felt it must go on for ever. Surely, surely no man could ever be made captive in these surroundings.

They sat silent a long time, like statues carved from the primitive rock upon which they sat. Then Nemarluk grunted.

"Since your spirit father set you free upon earth," he said, "you have looked out many a night upon this."

"I love it," answered Deven shortly.

"I know, now, why you fear to leave here for the Wild Lands," said Nemarluk.

"Because I fear to lose my liberty," snarled Deven.

They were silent again. Then Nemarluk said: "But when I return with Chugulla's men and the Cahn-mah you will leave?"

"Yes."

"Why?"

"Because I fear that the whites, and the Jap men too may come more and more. The more they come, the less our warriors grow. It is best to kill off the whites before they become too many. Otherwise, we shall lose our liberty."

They gazed out silently. Far away below from the river trees a boobook owl was hooting "Wow-wow, wow-wow."

CHAPTER XXII

ECLIPSE

SEVERAL weeks passed. The patrol tried all they knew to learn news of Nemarluk but the station blacks shook sullen heads. Nemarluk was far away, they grunted. They knew nothing of him. Cared less.

The patrol rode away down river searching the wide stretches towards Blunder Bay.

Nemarluk laughed.

"They daren't tell," growled Deven. "But you are not as safe as you used to be. Bul-bul has his totem friends here and there. Those are the ones we do not know, the secret ones. But even they dare not tell while my men are about."

At night Nemarluk now ventured down from the cliffs to warily approach the station native camp. He always waited for a signal from one of Deven's men before gliding in from the night. Squatting by a fire with the people all around him, he felt happy. The life of a camp, even a strange camp, was home compared to his months of loneliness, camping like a hunted dingo among the rocks.

By and by the patrol came riding back up river. Nemarluk and Deven took to the cliffs. In a few days the patrol rode on bound for Timber Creek a hundred miles and more up river. They would refit at Timber Creek, then ride away out into the Wild Lands.

Nemarluk and Deven came down to the camp. Now the main fires were taken possession of by the renegades and cattle spearers, the wild men from the hills, to the delight of the women and children but glowering looks from the station boys. Deven's men did not care. There was much grunting and whispering from those dark groups around the fires, gleam of teeth, flash of eye, occasional rattle of spears.

Eagerly Nemarluk planned with them, naming warrior after warrior of Chugulla's tribe and his own who would join with them. Convincing them of security when they would cross the river; that even if hardpressed the Valley of the Dead was as safe as their own wild hideout; that the tribes away out there had no "tame blacks" among them; convincing them how easily they could get back again if plans went astray.

"Nothing will go wrong," growled Deven, "if we plan well first."

Night after night they discussed the winning of this hard fighting band to their way of thinking. Nemarluk, growing every day more confident, laughed often now. He was living again as the big chief; he could see himself leading a band of men such as no warrior had ever led before. He began to sleep nearer the camp. Deven, although his own men held this camp in terror, would seldom sleep anywhere but in the black shadows among the cliffs.

"I'm afraid of nothing," laughed Nemarluk to Deven's frown, "and I must show these men I fear nothing. If I dare not sleep near them what sort of a leader will they think I am?"

One night he arose with a smile, a very happy man. All was settled. On the morrow he was to start away to collect his own men and the best warriors from Chugulla's tribe, lead them here, and Deven's band would join him for good and all. He picked up his spears and his big chest swelled as he gazed down upon them. These would soon be his men.

"Ma-muck," he farewelled with a flash of teeth and stepped away into the night.

And shadows arose with him.

Quite a distance from camp Nemarluk seemed to melt into the blackness of a thicket, a tangle of scrub and cane and vines. He crawled right away in, settled himself down, and coiled up for sleep with a smile upon his lips.

They allowed him plenty of time to fall sound asleep, then Bul-bul crawled in after him. The others

waited, their ears strained for the first noise.

Nemarluk awoke to find the great arms of Bul-bul around him. To the crashing of the canes and vines the others rushed in and threw themselves upon the struggling men.

Again and again Nemarluk threw them off, but always the vines entangled them, dragged them down again, a mass of snarling, struggling men. Saplings bent, roosting birds fluttered away with startled squawks. But they handcuffed Nemarluk at last, and lay there panting upon him, all entangled in the very canes and vines that were to have warned him of approaching enemies.

When Nemarluk gasped his strength back he tugged desperately at his wrists. Bul-bul laughed. Nemarluk would never break that steel.

They forced him out of the thicket, anxious to get as far away from the camp as quickly as possible. They started away up river. One man started running, to carry the news to Constable Fitzer. Presently they stopped and from a hiding place brought forth clothes. The trackers dressed. Then into the dawn the long march started.

All day long Nemarluk lived in the wildest hope that Deven would attempt a rescue. But Deven's men thought Nemarluk had crossed the river at dawn and set out on his long journey to collect his men. When night came the face of Nemarluk looked almost old. He plodded on, almost hopeless.

There came a cold morning, just before the dawn. They lay asleep on the bank of the Bullo River. Cautiously, Nemarluk opened his eyes. Beside him snored the big form of Bul-bul. On the other side of Bul-bul there slept another tracker with close by him the black forms of several of Bul-bul's totem clansmen.

Inch by inch Nemarluk began working his body toward the river bank. Once deep into that friendly water and he would get away, he cared not for his manacled hands. Black night was giving way to the first cold grey of dawn. Nemarluk's heart began thumping violently, he was very near the sloping edge of the river, he saw the cold gleam of water. He took a deep breath, a last glance at the sleeping trackers.

Bul-bul's eyes were open, a grin at the corner of his mouth. Nemarluk rolled down over the bank as Bul-bul leaped. As Nemarluk hit the water Bul-bul was on top of him, Nemarluk's manacled hands snatching for Bul-bul's throat. To the splash, the sleepers awoke, sprang for the bank. Nemarluk was dragging Bul-bul under. Bul-bul's hand snatched for his belt and gripped a spare set of handcuffs. In the nick of time he swung the cuffs fair upon Nemarluk's head.

They dragged Nemarluk back to the bank; the fight had gone out of him.

They met the white policeman. And then it was a long, long march to Darwin—and Fanny Bay Jail. He saw it again, the big fence that shut out the sweet, free bush, that shut out liberty.

Nemarluk died, only recently. Died of a broken heart.